For Cara, Felicity
and Flora

This first edition,
first published in 2019
to mark the 500th anniversary
of the death of
Leonardo Da Vinci.

Follow Agnès's journey

facebook.com/agnesandthebirdman

Amboise

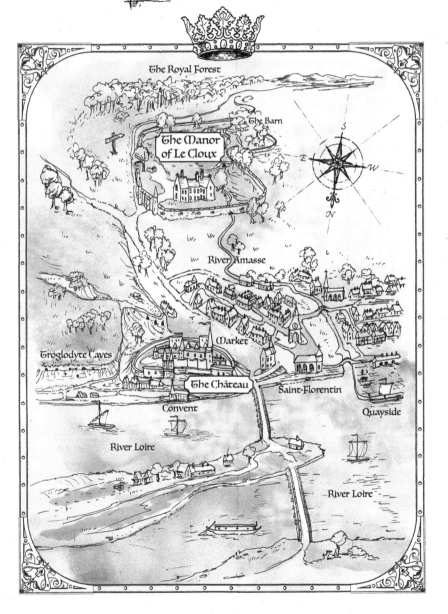

The Royal Forest

The Barn

The Manor
of Le Cloux

River Amasse

Market

Troglodyte Caves

The Château

Saint-Florentin

Convent

Quayside

River Loire

River Loire

Tuscany, Italy - AD 1505

Upon a rocky ledge, high above Swan Mountain quarry, there perched a peculiar bird of wood and sailcloth. Ropes creaked; broad wings swayed. Struts bent and flexed with every gust and flurry as the curious contraption teetered over the abyss.

Harnessed beneath the belly of the bird, a skinny young lad held on tightly. The boy looked to the sky where a dark raven circled with steely eyes and piercing caws that echoed all through the quarry below.

The Master stepped forwards. His cloak fluttered about his knees as he laid a hand on the bird's willow frame and slowly drew breath.

"Think, Francesco!" he said. "Think what everyone will say when they hear of this day." The boy shrugged.

"What will they say, Master?" he mumbled.

"They will say, *There goes the boy who flew.*" The skinny lad gripped the levers of the bird-machine tightly.

"What if I can't?" he said, his voice aquiver.

"Nonsense," said the Master, running his fingers through wild hair and whiskers. "It is a mathematical certainty—the Cigno will fly." As the boy glanced down over the steep rocky ledge and trembled, his master went around checking buckles and fastenings one last time. "Once you are aloft, circle around as high as you can and bring her down beyond those rocks," he said, "and remember, Francesco, those who dare, shall live for evermore." The boy closed his eyes tightly.

"I dare, I dare," he kept saying through gritted teeth. The Master stepped back.

"The triumph of this day will fill the universe with wonder and amazement," he uttered. Then, reaching up with both arms, he raised his voice to the heavens. "Vola!" he cried loudly. The great wooden bird groaned as it leaned over the precipice and offered its flaxen wings to the sky. With a wild cry, the skinny boy leapt from the jutting outcrop into the void.

As canvas billowed and ropes pulled tight, the bird-machine hung in the air like a leaf on the breeze. Nesting chicks fell silent, lizards scurried into rocky crevices, and doves flapped to the safety of the treetops.

Then, turning earthward, it embarked upon its terrible descent. The Master stepped to the edge and looked down with wide eyes as the machine tumbled and twisted. He gazed on in horror as it jolted from crag to crag—from boulder to boulder—tearing and splitting apart against the rocks. Wings crumpled. Struts and fastenings splintered like shattered bones. Above the tearing of canvas and cracking of wood, the boy's anguished cries rang out. Clutching the folds of his cloak tightly, the Master watched and waited for the tumble of rocks to subside.

"Francesco... Francesco!" he hollered down as the dust settled over tangled ruins. "Are you all right?" But all he heard back was the crack and snap of branches and the scurry of creatures in the undergrowth below.

1

Fourteen years later - Amboise, France

Agnès waited in the shadows and watched for her next victim. As she peered out from her dark recess, a knot pulled tight inside. Tucking a stray wisp of hair beneath her hood, she breathed deeply and swallowed hard. Bright sunlight brimmed over the walls of the Royal Château of Amboise and splashed onto the cobbled streets below. Agnès felt its warmth on her pale skin.

The market square soon bustled to life with townsfolk, picking and weaving their way past noisy poultry, barrows of shellfish and boxes of leafy winter vegetables. Two women chattered like noisy parakeets by the water fountain. One was wearing a string of pearly beads. The other had a silver brooch pinned to her gown. When the clocktower bell chimed out the passing hour, Agnès made her move, closing in like a wild animal stalking its prey. As she drew near, however, her steps faltered.

Across the way stood a lone dark figure. He was dressed all in black, from the plume of his broad hat down to the heels of his shiny boots. Marshal Lupus, the thief catcher of Amboise, was surveying the busy throng, watching the comings and goings of the crowded marketplace like a hawk.

Agnès lingered by the tavern door where dark thoughts flocked like hungry ravens, ready to peck at the remains of her wilting courage. Waiting for Lupus to move on, she recalled the time she had tried to work loose a pair of silver buckles from a man's shoes. Crawling on hands and knees in the crowded square, she found herself staring into the slobbering jowl of his enormous bloodhound. She had been lucky to escape that time, scuttling off through a forest of legs on all fours as the beast snarled and snapped on the end of its leash.

Taking up her search once more, Agnès noticed a big nobleman heading towards the meat stall. He was wearing a fine crimson cloak with an expensive red ruby pinned to it. The fellow was bald. He had small beady eyes and a barrel-shaped belly. Every step seemed a great bother to him. He kept stopping to wipe his brow and puff out his ruddy cheeks.

Agnès plotted her every move with all the forethought and stratagem of a chess master. She would walk over and stumble at the nobleman's feet. He would reach out a chivalrous hand to help her up. She would snatch the jewel and hide it up her sleeve, whilst thanking him for his kindness. By the time he realised his precious ruby was missing, she would be long gone. A man of his size hardly stood a chance of catching her, she thought. Her plan was sure.

As she stepped forwards, however, a shabbily dressed woman carrying caged songbirds crossed her path. The birds chirped and flitted noisily, flashing their bright feathers. The woman, cooing like a mother dove to her chicks, stopped to rest her calloused arms. By the time she had moved on, the bald nobleman in the crimson cloak was nowhere to be seen.

Cursing the birdwoman for getting in the way, Agnès stepped back beneath a sign that hung over the apothecary shop doorway. Peering through swollen squares of glass, she looked in at all the bottles and jars, lined up along the shelves. Misshapen figures flitted like spectres between the panes.

When Agnès glanced around, she saw a white-bearded stranger in a black cloak and a tall young man clutching a pile of books. The old man walked slowly, waving his arms as he spoke. With every sweeping gesture, his young accomplice would nod agreeably. Agnès noticed a pigskin purse tied to his belt. The pouch hung heavily and she considered how to get it from him without being seen. She turned to face the shop window and listened. But the old man spoke curious words from some far-off place and she understood nothing of what he said. When they reached the doorway, bells jangled, and the two strangers went inside.

Through the window, Agnès could see the old man pointing up at shelves, and the shopkeeper, Monsieur Quignaux, lifting down jars full of bright pigments. As the strangers deliberated over all the powders and potions lined up along the countertop, she felt in her pocket for a knife to cut free the young man's purse. She ran her thumb over the blade, but it was dull and hardly up to the task.

7

Keeping a sharp lookout for the Marshal, Agnès wandered off in search of a better prospect. Turning back the way she had come, she caught sight of the bald nobleman in the crimson cloak—the one with the red ruby pin. He was standing by a market stall, prodding cheeses with his chubby finger. This time Agnès would not halt or falter. She walked over and floundered at the big nobleman's feet. At first, he barely noticed, so she grabbed her ankle and let out a cry for help. The man looked down. He reached out a hand. Agnès got to her feet and grabbed at the folds of his crimson cloak.

"Thank you Monsieur, how clumsy of me," she said, snatching the ruby pin and tucking it up her sleeve. "You've done me a great kindness, sir."

"My pleasure," said the man with a nod. As he straightened himself up and brushed himself down, the expression on his face dropped.

"My ruby," he blurted, patting his chest and glaring at Agnès scornfully. As Agnès stepped back, she stumbled into a woman carrying a basket of eggs. The basket toppled and eggs smashed everywhere.

"Stop, thief!" yelled the man. Slipping and sliding over the cobbles, Agnès started to run. She spotted Marshal Lupus heading her way, the plume of his hat prancing as he marched along. He was looking right at her with that steely gaze of his. Turning on her heel, Agnès darted back towards the main thoroughfare where she knew of a place to hide. Between the cobbler's shop and the tavern was a gap just wide enough for her to squeeze through. When she got there, the shabby birdwoman had set out her cages, barricading the way. Seeing the look of panic in Agnès's eyes, the birdwoman lifted aside her cages and let her through.

Crouching low like a frightened creature in its burrow, Agnès regarded every stir and sound. A rat twitched in the darkness. Water dripped from a high place with a steady drip-drop, and her heart raced as she peered out and listened for the click of the Marshal's heels.

When bells jangled, she looked out along the line of jutting shop fronts. She saw the white-bearded stranger and his young companion step out from the apothecary shop doorway. They were heading her way. When they reached the shabby birdwoman's cages, the old man stopped and began tapping each one in turn. The birds chirruped and sang, vying to be the chosen one.

When Lupus stepped out from the crowd, he too stopped right by the birdwoman's cages. The bald nobleman was only a few steps behind him, puffing out his cheeks and ranting angrily about his stolen gem. Agnès did her best not to make a sound.

"She was no more than a child," said the nobleman. "A pale and scrawny thing in a grey hood." Marshal Lupus raised his cane and struck the ground with it. The chirruping birds fell silent. He turned to the birdwoman.

"Have you seen a pale young girl in a grey hood?" he said. The birdwoman bent low and busied herself, picking birdseed from the cracks between the cobbles. She shook her head.

"What about you?" Lupus asked the two strangers. "Have you seen her?"

"Is she in some sort of trouble?" said the old man.

"The girl is a thief and no mistake," said the Marshal. "I advise you to keep your wits about you."

Lupus strode off, the plume of his hat bristling as he went. The bald nobleman, clutching the folds of his cloak, followed after him. When they had gone, the bearded stranger went back to prodding bird cages. He had the look of a sorcerer, Agnès thought. She had heard tales of wizards with long white beards and black cloaks. Perhaps the young man was the sorcerer's apprentice, with books full of spells and enchantments.

"What price are your songbirds?" asked the old man, turning to the bird seller.

"Two sous apiece," said the shabby birdwoman through blackened teeth. The old man gave a nod and his young companion untied his purse and drew out a few coins. He handed them to the bird seller and the old sage picked out what must have been the scrawniest finch of all. It was a common brown linnet with a blush of red feathers.

After settling the transaction, the old man set off carrying the little bird in its cage. Crossing over, he set it down by the water pump. He reached out a bony hand and unclasped the cage door.

"I bet he turns it into a dragon," thought Agnès, craning her neck for a better view. She half expected the bird to grow and transform into a magical beast of some kind. Perhaps it would turn into an enchanted eagle, a griffon or a fearsome sphinx. Then she would know for sure that the old man was a sorcerer. She thought his apprentice might have a spell for it in one of his books and had bought such a potion from Monsieur Quignaux.

The old man held up the cage and uttered strange words.

"Vola libero!" he cried. The little bird ruffled its feathers. Hopping over to the cage door, it twitched and fluttered— and, like a leaf on a blustery day, it rose up to the sky and flew off over the rooftops.

2

Light from a small candle flickered over craggy limestone walls. It brightened every corner of the tiny hilltop cavern, casting a warm glow on the face of Mother Mary. Agnès reached for a fresh taper and lit it. She placed it beside the little wooden statue, standing in its hollowed-out niche in the cavern wall.

"Forgive me, Holy Mother," she said. The very thought of

the bald nobleman's horrified scowl and the marshal's cold stare filled her with dread. Lupus had now seen her face and wouldn't stop looking until she was caught.

Taking out the red ruby pin, she held it up to the light. The jewel burned like a fiery hot ember in her hand, and she shuddered to think that such a small thing had almost brought about her ruin. She would gladly sell it to anyone willing to pay her a few meagre sous, with no questions asked. She tucked the pin away and tried not to think of it a moment longer.

Agnès glanced around in the dim light of her clifftop hideaway. In one corner was her bed of dry straw. On a rocky ledge stood a bundle of half-burnt candles that she had stolen from the Chapel of Saint-Denis when the priest wasn't looking. Propped up beside them was a shard of mirror glass. When Agnès gazed at her reflection, the words of the bald nobleman echoed in her mind. He had called her a pale and scrawny thing—a ragged thief. Agnès knew she was more than that. When she looked in the glass, she saw determined eyes. Her hair, the colour of autumn leaves, grew wild and free. Even the Reverend Mother back at the convent said she was a rare and precious flower.

Agnès felt her stomach groan. She went over to a sturdy iron chest in the far corner of the cavern. It was the kind that sailors keep their gunpowder dry in. She opened it up and took out a wedge of cheese and a crust of bread. Breaking off a corner of each, she went over to the cavern entrance and sat on a big stone to eat her supper. It wasn't much, but Agnès was glad for what she could get. Looking out over the rooftops below, she let the cares of the day float away as fleeting birds circled overhead, and the sun's red orb sank low over the flowing waters of the Loire.

It had been months since she had come to live in her clifftop cavern. It was one of many that had been dug out of the rock-face long ago by the ancient Troglodyte people. At first, Agnès had felt afraid to sleep alone in her cave. She had heard tales of an old hag who, some said, once cursed the place. Now she told those same tales to keep others away. In her version, the old woman had one eye and turned children into beetles and slugs that she fed to her pet toad. Now, with Mother Mary watching from her niche in the cavern wall, she felt much more at ease.

Agnès had done what she could to make her cavern comfortable. She had swept it clean and had gathered fresh straw for her bed. She kept her food and belongings safe from rats and mice in the old sea chest.

As she perched on her rock, nibbling bread and cheese, Agnès watched the townsfolk of Amboise wending their way across the bridge of seven arches. She could see boatmen tying up their flat-bottomed riverboats to moorings along the banks. Seeing rich folk in their carriages, she wondered what noble guests were on their way to the Royal Château to see the King and Queen. Darting swifts swarmed over the high turrets, and the castle walls burned brightly in the orange glow of the setting sun.

When a dark shadow passed over the cavern entrance, Agnès glanced up and saw a fluttering creature descending on beating wings.

"Magellan!" she cried out as a large black crow landed beside her. Cawing loudly, the bird hobbled over like an old man on crutches. Agnès broke off a crust and held it out. "Where have you been?" she said. "I was beginning to think you had forgotten me." Magellan snatched at the morsel.

He held it with his claw and pecked greedily. Agnès peeled off a sliver of cheese rind and tossed it down.

"Things have changed," she said. "Lupus just about had

me this time." She told Magellan all about the ruby pin and how she was almost caught by the Marshal. Magellan cawed. He flapped his wings at her mention of the white-bearded sorcerer and his apprentice. He ruffled his feathers when she got to the part where the two strangers bought a linnet and let it go without conjuring up the slightest bit of wizardry.

The sky was rapidly darkening. The orange glow that had bathed the Château walls, and flooded the town below, now washed away, leaving nothing but the shadowy silhouettes of rooftops and turrets.

Stars began to appear and Agnès thought back to the day she ran away from the convent and came to live in her cavern hideaway. It had been months. Since then, the Great Bear had ranged silently through its vast celestial wilderness, guided on its way by the North Star. Agnès looked down at Magellan.

"I have to go," she said. "It won't be safe for me here in Amboise until things have blown over."

Magellan settled by the cavern entrance with his head beneath his wing. Agnès sat stroking his silky feathers. When the air grew chill, she brushed the crumbs from her lap and went back inside. Lighting a fresh candle, she looked across at Mother Mary. As she gazed at the little wooden carving, her thoughts turned fleetingly to her own mother. She pictured her long hair and her broad smile. When she closed her eyes, she could see her mama sitting on the cottage doorstep, peeling apples. She could almost hear her singing softly as ribbons of green fell about her feet. Such thoughts were hard to bear and she quickly put them out of her mind.

Searching around in the old sea chest, Agnès took out her book of bird drawings. It was full of sketches that she had done to while away the dark winter evenings. Her first drawing was of a sparrow-hawk. After seeing it on a fence one day, she had carried a vision of it in her mind. Later on, by candlelight, she had captured the scene with chalks and charcoal. Another drawing was of a wild red-breasted goose. Rubbing the chalk in circles, she had smudged and smoothed the bird's plumage until it was as soft as feather down. There were sketches of eagles, owls, swans, geese, finches and doves. Each one was preserved forever like flowers, pressed between the pages of a book.

Her favourite bird was drawn on the back of an old sea chart. It had majestic wings and a long tail, like the streamers of a kite. The creature hatched out in her dreams one night, fledging when she awoke with chalky feathers of red, yellow and blue. Agnès gazed at the bird in the flickering candlelight. She told herself that if she had such wings, she would fly across the great ocean to the New World. She would search for her papa in that strange land that every seafarer was talking about.

Taking out a fresh sheet of paper and a quill, she rested on the lid of the old sea chest and started to write him a letter.

17

Dear Papa,

Now that the winter is over, every day seems warmer and brighter. Magellan is back, but I am afraid he relies on me far too much. Last night I dreamt that you were here. You were telling me such wonderful stories about the places you have seen.

When you return from across the sea, we shall walk in the forest and sleep on the hillside where we can look up at the stars together. Then we shall have such a long talk.

Tomorrow I am going away. I will come back when it is safe. If you should arrive before I do, promise to wait for me here in Amboise.

With all my love, Agnes

When she had finished, Agnès reached for a little wooden trinket box. It was one she had taken from the jeweller's shop. With her knife, she scratched her father's name onto the lid. Folding up the letter, she tucked it inside the box. She closed the lid and slipped it in the pocket of her mantle. Rummaging in the old sea chest, she picked out a few things for the journey ahead. She took out a knife, a lump of salted meat, some nuts and her last bit of cheese.

It was then that Agnès remembered about the Royal Hunt. The occasion had all but slipped her mind. At first light of day, the King and his court would be setting off for the Royal Forest. Every nobleman and duke for miles around would be there with their hawks and owls, eager to show off their latest skills. It would be a good time to slip away unnoticed. Snuffing out her candle, she nestled down on her bed of straw, thinking about the birds and wondering where the Fates might take her next.

3

As the bells of Saint-Florentin and Saint-Denis rang out early the next morning, Agnès peered through the rocky portal of her hilltop cavern. She watched the night sky melt away as the sun seeped into the starry expanse. Magellan had already gone. He was always an early bird, but Agnès felt disappointed that he hadn't waited to see her go. Getting dressed, she laced her boots, buttoned up her mantle and checked in the old sea chest to make sure she hadn't forgotten anything.

As she scrambled down the hillside to the pathway below, the tendrils of an idea began to twist and twine in her mind. First, she would go in search of Clovis Merlin. He would pay her a few sous for the red ruby pin. With the money, she would leave Amboise and set off for Tours where she would be safe from Lupus. Foraging in her pocket, Agnès fished out her scrap of dried meat. She bit off a corner and chewed as she walked.

All along the Château walls, ensigns hung limp in the cool morning air. A woman, swilling her doorstep, looked around as Agnès passed by. A man, sharpening his knives, glanced up. She stepped out of the way for a pedlar whose heavy load of pots and pans clanked and rattled as he trudged along.

Up ahead, the blowing of horns and baying of hounds grew loud. When she rounded the corner by the castle rampart and looked along the thoroughfare, Agnès saw a great mustering of riders by the roadside. Unable to get across, she hid in a narrow crevice by the rampart and watched as the hunt got underway. Each rider wore a thick glove and held aloft a magnificent bird of prey. There were kestrels, merlins and peregrines, as well as eagle owls with their tufts pricked up like hat feathers. Hooves clopped, wings flapped, and wild screeches echoed all along the Château walls.

King François rode out astride a white stallion, holding a fine hooded falcon. A bow hung from his shoulder and his quiver was adorned with the royal motif of the white salamander.

All around the market square, hunters gathered with spears and bows. There were beaters wielding long sticks and trappers carrying nets. Women, wearing bonnets and cloaks, sported short bows and cudgels, ready for their part in the kill.

The tramp of feet and hooves stirred up clouds all along the way as the hunting party moved off. When the cacophony of horns and hounds faded in the distance, Agnès came out from her hiding place and continued on her way towards the clocktower. In her quest to find Clovis Merlin, she crossed over the little stone bridge that led beyond the Amasse to the waterfront.

Along the banks of the Loire, fishermen sat mending their nets and baiting their lines. Agnès walked beyond the quay to the water's edge and stopped for a few moments. The sun danced on the water and minnows darted back and forth in the shallows. Reaching into the pocket of her mantle, she took out the wooden trinket box with her papa's letter inside. Stooping down, she placed it in the water and gave it a push. The little trinket box slipped away. Agnès knew it stood little chance of ever reaching the sea. But she would send it anyway, with a silent prayer that it might wash up on some distant shore where her father would discover it.

As she turned and started to walk away, Agnès caught sight of a ragged boy. He was small and thin, wearing only a roughly woven shirt and a pair of torn hose that hung around his scabby knees.

"Wait, don't go!" said the boy. Agnès walked a little faster.

"Come back!" called out the boy.

"Leave me alone," said Agnès.

"I want you to teach me," said the boy. "Show me how to take things without being seen."

"I don't know what you're talking about," said Agnès, doing her best to get away.

"Yes, you do," said the boy, tripping and dancing like a troublesome sprite as he tried to catch up. "I've seen you do it." He reached into his pocket and pulled out a string of pearly beads. "I can get money for these, can't I?" he said.

"Where did you get those?" said Agnès.

"A lady dropped them," said the boy. "Look, the string is broken."

"If Lupus catches you with those beads, he'll take you away," said Agnès.

"Take me where?" said the boy. Agnès pointed.

"To the tower," she said. "You'll be locked away in a dark place."

"Then show me how to keep from getting caught," the boy pleaded. Agnès shook her head.

"This isn't a game," she insisted, pushing him away and running off. When she stopped and looked around, the ragged boy was gone.

Arriving back at the quayside, where boats were being loaded, Agnès kept a sharp lookout for Clovis Merlin. He was small and thin with a stooped back, and would be easy to pick out, even in all the bustle of merchants going back and forth. Whenever she had something worth selling, she would go to Merlin first. Others were less trustworthy. Like the old woman who promised to pay her two sous for a hair clasp, but never did.

Standing around watching for longer than she would have liked, Agnès grew tired of waiting. If Clovis Merlin failed to show up, she wondered what she would do. Without money, she had no way of paying for her passage by boat to Tours. Her only other option was to walk there. It would take days and there would be untold dangers along the way. The road led through the forest where she might encounter robbers and wolves—or, worse still, the King's men.

Looking around, Agnès noticed a dark figure coming her way. The instant she saw him, she knew it was Marshal Lupus. There was no doubt about it. He was wielding his stick like a beater at the hunt, checking behind every box and barrel he came to. When the Marshal looked over, Agnès quickly turned away. The ruby pin was still in her pocket. If she ran, Lupus would know she had something to hide. If he saw her, he would surely recognise her face. She began to walk away slowly.

Just then, a fleeting figure darted out. It was the ragged boy. When the Marshal saw him, he instantly gave chase. Reaching out, he caught the young wretch by the arm.

The boy was clutching his string of pearly beads. Lupus tightened his grip.

"Thieving urchin," he said. The boy squealed and squirmed. He kicked and flailed. But Lupus wasn't about to let him get away. Agnès watched as the thief-catcher clamped an iron on his arm and hauled him off. With her hood up and her head down, she hurried back across the stone bridge. Passing by the church of Saint-Florentin, she headed for the road to Tours, anxious to be on her way.

4

Beyond the streets of Amboise, the road twisted and snaked towards the Royal Forest. Shafts of sunlight reached through the branches of tall trees, painting dappled patches all along the way. Up ahead, Agnès could see the rooftops and chimneys of a red-brick manor house, surrounded on every side by a high garden wall. As she drew near, she noticed a grim-faced watchman scowling down from his tower. The sharp point of his long pike glinted in the light. Agnès scowled back then hurried off along a track beside the wall. A little further on, she heard cries and shouts coming from the other side. It sounded like children fighting and squabbling.

When she heard the clop of hooves up ahead, Agnès looked and saw two riders on dappled grey horses coming her way. She stepped up to the high garden wall and reached for a narrow crevice. With every grip and foothold, the crumbling stonework broke loose. The drooping branch of a tall tree hung over from the garden on the other side. Agnès grabbed hold of it and pulled herself up. When she swung her legs onto the branch, her kirtle snagged. She cursed and pulled it free. Gripping tightly, she clambered higher and higher.

The clopping of hooves grew loud and Agnès could see the two riders down below. They were dressed in the King's colours and carried long staffs and swords. Laughing and talking, neither of them noticed her up there as they passed beneath the green canopy. When they had gone, Agnès gazed into the distance from her treetop lookout. She could see the Royal Forest stretching out to the horizon. Looking back the other way, she could see the Château of Amboise and the tower where Lupus had taken the ragged boy. She felt awful about what had happened to him. But what could she do?

"It was all his own fault," she thought.

Clambering down, Agnès reached out with dangling legs and set her feet firmly on the copestone of the wall. A roosting dove flew off in a wild flutter as she edged her way along. Through the tangle of branches, she could see a lawn with grazing sheep. A stony path led off into a dense thicket. She spotted the watchman in his tower. He was facing the other way and hadn't noticed her up there.

Peering through the mass of foliage, Agnès saw someone in the garden below. It was an old man in a long scarlet robe. He was sitting on a log, beside a pool of water. As she looked on, she felt sure it was the same old fellow that had set the little bird free. His white hair and beard cascaded down like a silvery waterfall. His eyes were bright and alive.

Agnès watched as he stooped to pick up a handful of pebbles and began tossing them, one by one, into the pond. She looked on with intrigue as, with each splash and plop, he kept glancing down to sketch their patterns of watery ripples in a notebook that lay open on his lap.

When excited voices filled the air, Agnès turned and saw two children running across the lawn. One was a young girl in a blue velvet dress. The other was a small boy in red breeches. The girl was pulling on the boy's arm as he yelled wildly, trying his best to get away. Over by the house, she could see a tall young man in a floppy hat. He was setting up an artist's easel, propping apart the legs to stop it falling over. Agnès parted the branches for a better view. She saw it was the tall young apprentice who had been with the old man in the marketplace.

Holding a long thin brush, the young artist called for the children to come and sit still. But the girl was busy yelling, and the boy was bawling so loudly that neither of them heard a thing. As the children ran about, a plump-faced woman— wearing a black dress and white pinafore—came out from the manor house carrying a dish of sweetmeats. She grabbed the children by their arms.

"Come and sit for Melzi," she said, offering them comfits from her bowl. "How can he paint your picture if you won't be still?" As they sat eating sticky fruits, the tall young man quickly set to work, sketching lines and curves with swift dark strokes. The drawing quickly took shape. As the young artist sketched, the old man got up from his log by the pond and came over to inspect his work.

"Ben fatto, eccellente!" he said, stroking his beard and

patting the young fellow on the arm. "Prosegui!" As the young artist continued, the old man turned to the boy, sitting restlessly on his pedestal. Stooping low, he snatched him up and whirled him around in the air.

"Fly young François!" he cried, laughing as the boy flapped like a bird.

"Put him down!" demanded the woman in black. "How can Melzi draw the Prince with you whipping him up like that?"

When she heard a shout, Agnès knew at once that she had been spotted. She looked and saw the grim-faced watchman, standing in the bushes below her, scowling like a mean old bear in the woods.

"Get down!" demanded the watchman, jabbing with his long pike at her dangling legs. When Agnès pulled them up, she dislodged a large chunk of stone. The wall crumbled. She tried to hold on, but it was no use.

As the watchman's angry cries rang out, she fell from her lofty perch. A sudden rush of air snatched her breath away. With arms flailing wildly, and feet kicking, Agnès toppled head over heels in a whirlpool of wild commotion, crashing headlong through the mass of twisting branches and foliage to the garden below.

Holding a long thin brush, the young artist called
for the children to come and sit still.

5

When Agnès came to her senses, she could hear birds singing and children laughing in some far-off place. The smell of cut grass and blossoms wafted in through an open window. She could feel the warmth of the sun on her face and the caress of soft sheets against her skin. As more of her senses rallied, however, she grew aware of a dull ache in her side. A sharp pain coursed through her leg, reminding her of the watchman's angry cries and her frightful tumble from the garden wall.

Craning her neck, Agnès looked around and saw splendid things. She saw decorated plates and painted pottery on a high shelf. On the wall was a broad tapestry. It was a scene of hunters with bows, chasing a white stag—as well as bathing ladies beside a waterfall. The room was full of elaborate furnishings and fancy ornaments.

"I shouldn't be here," Agnès told herself.

Pushing back the covers, she slowly sat up. In a tall mirror, she saw her own reflection—a ghostly apparition, dressed in a white linen nightgown—staring back. Her face was completely ashen and she had a large bump on her forehead. Across the room, Agnès could see her own clothes, folded neatly on a chair. Pulling off the linen nightgown, she lowered herself onto shaky feet. She slowly made her way over to the chair and put on her kirtle and boots. She grabbed her coat and went over to the door. Her heart raced as she turned the handle. Peering out along a narrow landing, she listened to the thump and thud of people moving about down below.

When Agnès stepped out, floorboards creaked. Seeing a door further along the landing, she took another step. When she got to it, she slowly turned the handle and entered a darkened room. A thin trace of light stole in through a crack between the shutters across the way, tracing the outlines and edges of tables and chairs.

Stepping gingerly, Agnès made her way over to the window. She eased open the shutters and peered out. Down below was a path that led off through the garden, and a fountain with birds splashing about in it. Beyond the manor house wall, the turrets and ensigns of the Château rose up above the little town of Amboise.

Sunlight now flooded every corner of the room. All around, Agnès could see cabinets and tables, piled high with books and papers, writing implements and curious things. One large book lay open on a table. Its pages were thick and rough around the edges. On one side, drawn with great skill and artistry, was a picture of a damselfly with a slender body and gauze-like wings. On the opposite page were other insects. There were butterflies, dragonflies, mayflies and fireflies—all depicted in exquisite detail.

One table was cluttered with quills, nibs, chalks and thin sticks of charcoal. There were ink pots, jars of bright pigments and cockle shells with dried-up paints in them. On another table, Agnès noticed a curious metal sphere mounted on a pedestal. The shiny ball had segments, like an orange, with intricate swirls and patterns engraved on them.

When Agnès poked it, the metal sphere began to click and whirr. Like a flower unfurling in the morning light, it slowly opened. When the whirring stopped, a small mechanical bird, inside, opened wide its beak and began to sing. Its chorus was as sweet as any nightingale's.

When the singing and flapping stopped, Agnès continued to look around the room of books. She reached for a small volume bound in green leather that had gold lettering on the spine. She turned its pages. The book was full of sketches, of plants, trees, flowers and fruits. In another volume, she discovered ocean waves, rivers, waterfalls and storm clouds. Their motions were forever frozen in time. Some of the pictures were done in ink. Others, in chalk, were drawn on blue and red tinted paper.

Agnès reached for a large book with a pattern of wings painted on the cover. She opened it up. The volume was full of drawings of eagles, hawks, finches and owls. The birds looked so real, as though they might fly off the pages and into the room at any moment. She thought about her own drawings, tucked away in the old sea chest. She had always been proud of her efforts, but these birds were of a much higher order.

Hearing footsteps out on the landing, Agnès quickly closed up the book of birds. When the handle turned and the door creaked open, she looked for a place to hide. Ducking low, she hid under a table and kept perfectly still. From her hiding place, she watched as a plump-faced woman stepped into the room. It was the woman in black she had seen feeding sweets to the children earlier on. The woman glanced around for a few moments then went back out. As soon as she had gone, Agnès came out from beneath the table and hurried over to the window. She squeezed through the open casement and clambered down through twisting ivy that clung to the manor house wall. With her feet planted firmly on the path below, she glanced back up. The plump-faced woman in black was hanging out of the window, waving down at her.

"Don't leave—come back!" she called out. In her bid to get away, Agnès set off along the garden path towards the water fountain. As she stumbled along, a cool mist blew in her face and all the birds flew away. Beyond the shrubbery and neatly manicured gardens, the way grew wild and thorny. When she came to a steep embankment, she hitched up her skirts and scrambled down the incline, sliding and bumping as she went.

At the bottom of the rocky slope was a woodland path that ran beside a shallow stream. Agnès followed the stream until she came to the garden wall where it disappeared into a drain of moss-covered brickwork. She reached up and tried to get a grip on the wall. As loose masonry flaked and crumbled away in her fingers, she lowered her arms. There seemed to be no way out. Like a bird in a cage, she felt trapped.

6

Retracing her steps along the stream, Agnès looked for another way out. She listened to the babble of the brook and the coo of doves. Through the trees, she could see the watchman making his way along a high embankment.

He had with him a big hound dog that tugged on its leash, sniffing and snuffling in the undergrowth as it went. Stepping from the path and crossing over the stream, Agnès pushed through a dense thicket. She could smell the earthy aroma of mouldering leaves as she made her way deeper into the woods. Brushing aside twigs and branches that hindered the way, she emerged at last from the trees into a small clearing.

In the middle of the clearing was an old barn. Its red-brick walls were overgrown with ivy, and the roof was covered with mossy shingles. Agnès went over. Hinges creaked as she pushed open the barn doors and let in the sunlight. The place smelt of wood shavings and pine tar. All around, she could see stacks of sawn timber, piles of ropes, and workbenches cluttered with carpenters tools. Up ahead, strange spindly objects hung from the roof timbers. Made of thin sticks, tied together with string, one was shaped like a bird. Its wings and tail were covered with silk. When Agnès reached up and touched it, the bird bobbed and twirled about. Another of the spindly objects was shaped like a dragonfly. One had wings like a bat.

Deep in the belly of the barn, a great monster brooded silently in the darkness. With enormous wings, it had the look of a dragon, slain in battle and hung up as a trophy by its vanquisher. Straining her eyes in the dim light, Agnès saw that the beast was made of wood, fastened together with ropes and straps. Its wings reached out to the walls of the barn. A knotted rope hung down. When she reached up and pulled on the frayed end, the monster awoke from its slumber and groaned. Agnès stumbled back and fell amongst the sawdust and wood shavings. She heard a voice and looked up. Standing in the shadows was the old man with the long white beard.

"So, you have discovered the Falco!" he said, his eyes lighting up. Agnès scrambled to her feet. She didn't know what to say.

"What do you think of her?" the old man asked.

"But what is it?" said Agnès, rather nervously.

"My latest flying machine," said the old man, taking hold of the wing to steady it.

"You built a flying machine?" said Agnès, brushing sawdust from her mantle. The old man gave a nod. Light shone in through a hole in the barn wall, illuminating his noble brow. He was wearing a leather apron and had a bundle of papers tucked beneath his arm.

"For years it has been my greatest dream," he said.

"Are you a sorcerer?" said Agnès. The old man laughed.

"Wizardry and magic are nothing but hen's teeth and horsefeathers," he said. "I study the laws of Nature and would sooner learn from the birds than the faeries."

"Then you are a birdman?" said Agnès. The old man smiled and nodded.

"Yes, I suppose I am indeed a birdman. And you?"

"My name is Agnès." The Birdman cleared away all the clutter from his workbench and unrolled the bundle of papers he was carrying.

"Here, let me show you what I mean," he said. Agnès looked on with intrigue as the Birdman showed her a drawing of a strange contraption with bat-like wings.

"The Pipistrello was my first ever flying machine," he said. He spoke of the day his young apprentice, Giacomo Salai, leapt from a high wall with it strapped to his back.

"Did he fly?" asked Agnès. The Birdman shook his head.

"No," he said. "But what I learnt from the endeavour was that the human arm has nowhere near the power to flap like a bat's wing." Agnès was hardly surprised to hear it. The Pipistrello looked more like a carnival costume than a flying machine.

The Birdman unrolled another of his drawings. It was of a much more complicated machine, with wings that were attached to handles, much like the oars of a rowing boat. It also had stirrups that could be pedalled by the feet.

"I called this one the Cigno," said the Birdman. "It was designed to harness the entire muscle-power of the human body, getting the legs to lend their strength to the arms." Stroking his beard, he recalled the day his other apprentice, Francesco Melzi, made the attempt.

"We climbed to a very high ridge overlooking Swan Mountain quarry," he recalled. "Melzi was to be the first among mortals to fly." He described the moment the boy jumped from the rocky precipice, pulling and pedalling with all his might.

"And did he fly?" Agnès asked.

"The attempt was a complete disaster," said the Birdman, "and Melzi swore he would never try again."

"What happened to the Cigno?" asked Agnès.

"It lay in ruins at the bottom of the quarry," said the Birdman. "I had no choice but to abandon it there."

Agnès wondered if the old man was simply fooling himself about being able to build a flying machine.

"If humans were meant to fly, wouldn't they have been born with wings?" she said. The Birdman frowned.

"Not necessarily," he replied. He unrolled yet another of his drawings. Agnès recognised it at once. It was a detailed plan of the wooden contraption of sticks and struts that now hung from the barn roof. The Birdman reached up and patted it as though checking the withers of a fine steed.

"What makes you think it will fly?" said Agnès.

"If my calculations are correct, then it is a mathematical certainty," said the Birdman. Agnès looked up at the machine's slender framework and wings. She pictured the Falco soaring majestically over forests and hills like a hawk, bursting through the clouds and swooping low over the rooftops. As she closed her eyes, she could almost hear the rush of air whistling past its wings.

When hinges creaked and a dog barked, Agnès turned and saw a dark figure silhouetted in the open doorway of the barn. It was the watchman. His mean-looking hound was tugging at its leash and sniffing the air with its wet snout.

"There you are," said the watchman, scowling angrily.

The Birdman stepped forwards.

"Relax, Hugo," he said. "The young lady is with me." The watchman huffed testily.

"That girl is trouble if you ask me," he said.

"Nonsense," said the Birdman. "Can't you see she's hurt?"

"But we don't know who she is," railed the watchman. "That will be all, Hugo," said the Birdman. Agnès leaned against the workbench to steady herself as the watchman slowly backed away.

"Take no notice of him," said the Birdman. "Hugo is only doing his job."

"I should go now," said Agnès. "I don't want to cause you

any more trouble." The Birdman furrowed his brow.

"But you're hardly well enough to go anywhere," he said. "That was quite a fall you had earlier on."

"I'll be fine," Agnès insisted. "I can manage well enough on my own."

"Let me summon your parents," said the Birdman. Agnès winced.

"You can't," she said. "They're not here." The Birdman frowned.

"Then your guardians must be sent for."

"I have no guardians," said Agnès. The old man tugged at his beard.

"You have no parents or guardians—who takes care of you?"

"I take care of myself," said Agnès. The Birdman shook his head.

"That won't do," he said. After a moment's thought, his eyes lit up. "Maturina, my housekeeper, can be your guardian until you are well again."

"How long will that be?" said Agnès.

"A week of bed rest is what you need," said the Birdman. Agnès gasped.

"A week!" she said. "I can't stay that long."

"Of course, you are free to go whenever you like," said the Birdman. "But if anything should happen to you, I would never forgive myself." Agnès winced all the more as the pain in her side grew worse.

"Don't worry about me," she said, trying hard not to show her discomfort.

"At least stay for dinner," said the Birdman. "My housekeeper, Maturina, is a wonderful cook." Agnès felt her stomach groan and her mouth water.

"Are you sure?" she said.

"I'm certain of it," said the Birdman, rolling up his drawings. "I'll have the maid sort out something for you to wear. Be ready by five o'clock."

The Birdman led the way back to the manor house. As they walked along the woodland path and crossed over the shallow stream by way of a small bridge, Agnès thought about the Birdman's promise of dinner. She hadn't eaten properly in days, and it had been months since she had shared a meal with others. Having almost forgotten what it was like to dine at a table, she worried about forgetting her manners or saying something awkward. Despite her unease, however, she no longer felt the urge to run away. She thought that she could trust the Birdman and knew that, within the walls of the manor house, she would be safe from Lupus.

7

Waiting in the upstairs room where she first woke up after her fall, Agnès looked around at all the fancy furnishings and ornaments. As well as a large bed, there was a tall mirror, a wide cupboard and an expensive-looking dressing table. Painted plates and vases with flowers, Chinese dragons and exotic birds of paradise on them were lined up along a shelf.

Agnès gazed at the tapestry of hunters and bathing damsels. She looked up and saw glittering glass beads that hung like frozen crystals from a chandelier above her head. Never had she seen such splendour. The convent was plain and gloomy by comparison. Her cavern was dark and drab. This place was full of light and wonder.

On the dresser was a shallow silver dish with scalloped edges like a shell. Agnès went over and picked it up. The dish was small enough to fit in the pocket of her mantle. She ran her finger along the edge and turned it over in her hand. Hearing a knock on the door, however, she put it down and took a step back.

"Come in!" She called out. The door opened wide and a

young maid walked into the room carrying a large bundle.

"The Master sent these," she said. Wearing a pale green gown, the maid looked similar in age to Agnès. Her hair and eyes were of the darkest brown. Agnès noticed something different about the way she spoke.

"You're not from around here are you?" she said.

"I come from England," said the maid, laying her bundle down on the bed. "My name is Anne—I'm one of Queen Claude's maids of honour." She unrolled a blue silk gown and began smoothing out the creases. The dress was very fine. It had long sleeves and a frilled collar.

"It's like something from a painting," said Agnès.

"Try it on," said Anne. Agnès hesitated. She felt awkward about getting undressed right then and there. "It's my job to help," Anne explained. Agnès went behind the tall mirror and took off her ragged old kirtle and shift. Lifting the blue silk dress over her head, she slipped it on and stepped back out.

"It fits perfectly," said Anne, lacing the gown up at the back and stooping down to straighten the hem. Agnès felt uncomfortable. Never in her life had she worn such a dress.

"I hope these are your size too," said the maid, holding out a pair of matching slippers. Agnès perched on the bed and put them on. She got up and looked at her reflection in the mirror. Her hair was a mess. She had a lump on her head, cuts and scratches on her face, and she felt like a fraud. Anne reached for an ivory-handled comb. She brushed it through Agnès's hair and teased out all the tangles.

"You could easily pass for a maid of honour at the Château."

"With a face like this?" said Agnès. She touched her bruised forehead and frowned.

"Let me help," said Anne. She opened up the dresser and took out a small ceramic pot. Dusting her hands with white powder, she smoothed it over Agnès's cuts and bruises until they had all but faded away. Agnès did her best to smile.

"I've never even seen inside the palace," she said. "What's it like?" Anne straightened the bedcovers and went over to the door.

"Come and see," she said, beckoning for Agnès to follow. She led the way down the twisting staircase to the kitchen. As they passed beneath a low arch, Anne reached for a lamp that hung on the wall.

"Stay close," she said, lighting the wick and continuing down yet another flight of steps.

"Where are we going?" Agnès asked.

"To the Château," replied Anne. Somewhat bewildered, Agnès followed after her. At the bottom of the stairwell, she entered a narrow passage. She followed the light and the sound of Anne's footsteps. As she went deeper, a cold chill started to creep up her legs. It was like being swallowed alive by a ravenous monster of the deep. The passage seemed to go on forever. When Agnès finally emerged and stepped out into the light, Anne was waiting.

"Where are we now?" she asked.

"At the foot of the tower," said Anne. "The passage lets the King visit the Master in secret, whenever he likes." Waving Agnès on, she led the way up a steep flight of winding steps. Agnès felt a dull ache in her side and grew dizzy as she climbed higher and higher.

"Mind your head," said Anne, ducking down as she passed beneath a low arch at the top. "Don't end up like King Charles."

"What happened to him?" said Agnès.

"He banged his head and died in this very spot," said Anne. Agnès stooped low as she followed the maid out onto the castle wall, high above the rooftops of Amboise.

Standing on the parapet side-by-side, Agnès and Anne gazed out towards the Royal Forest. Birds circled high above, and the River Amasse curled like a ribbon of silk, threading its way past the Manor of Le Cloux to the Loire. The chimneys and turrets of the manor house poked up through the canopy of trees. Agnès recalled climbing out of the upstairs window. That's what had led to her stumbling on the Birdman's little factory—hidden amongst the trees—his workshop full of tools and strange inventions. She turned to Anne.

"Have you ever seen the flying machine?" she asked.

"I've heard about it," said Anne.

"Do you think it will fly?" said Agnès.

"I'm not sure," said Anne. "The Master has lots of crazy ideas and inventions that he never finishes." As the clouds billowed overhead, Agnès wondered if the Birdman's dreams were perhaps no more than shifting clouds in a fanciful mind.

The white Château turrets reached to the sky and ensigns fluttered in the breeze. The palace was surrounded by neat gardens and wide lawns. Anne pointed to where the grass had been fenced off.

"That's where tournaments take place," she said. "We had our own tiltyard just like it back at Hever Castle in England. My sister Mary and I used to joust on our wooden hobby horses when we were small." It made Agnès smile to think of Anne and her sister trying to knock each other down in combat like that.

"You must be very rich, living in a castle," she said. Anne nodded.

"My father, Thomas Boleyn, is the Earl of Wiltshire," she said.

"Why did he send you here?" Agnès asked.

"Father wanted us to be educated in France."

"Have you been here long?"

"Two years," said Anne. "We sailed from England for the wedding of King Louis and Princess Mary."

"I'd love to sail on a big ship," said Agnès. "It sounds wonderful."

"It was awful," said Anne. "There was a storm. We were

blown onto the rocks and had to be rowed to Boulogne."

"Were you scared?"

"I would have been if Father hadn't been with me. He held my hand and kept telling me it would be all right."

"And the wedding?"

"It was a grand affair."

"What about your father—do you miss him?"

"He writes all the time," said Anne. "I keep his letters in a box under my bed. When I feel melancholy, I read them over and over." Agnès thought about her own dear papa and how much she longed for a letter from him.

Anne spoke about her life at the Château. As well as her lessons in sewing and writing, she had attended many banquets and balls. In fact, she said, they were getting quite a bore. Agnès told Anne all about the convent. She recalled how grey and gloomy it was there. She told her about running away and living in a cavern. She recalled how, all winter long, she had burnt candles and sticks to keep herself warm.

The two girls talked constantly as they toured the Château. The place was immense and grand. Anne led the way inside and showed Agnès rooms full of expensive furnishings, fine paintings and elegant statues. Going from one vaulted room to the next, Anne said it was the finest Château in all of France. One of the rooms, a grand salon for entertaining guests, had been newly built with elaborate carvings of birds and beasts of every kind on the walls.

On their way back to the tower, Agnès and Anne stopped to watch a group of archers practising for a tournament. Each held a longbow and took turns, shooting at a mat of woven straw. After each shot, the archers stepped further and further back from the target. Soon their arrows were shooting high and far. One archer reached for a fancy cross-bow. Winding back the sinews with a handle, he inserted a bolt in the firing groove and took aim. The bolt shot off and struck the target dead centre.

Agnès was impressed by the power and accuracy of such a weapon. As they walked off, she noticed two men standing by the tower with their backs turned. One was wearing a black cape. The plume of his hat bobbed about as he spoke.

"Is there another way back to the manor?" she said, stopping dead in her tracks.

"Only through the streets," said Anne, "but it's not safe out there—thieves are everywhere."

"Can't we wait here a moment?" said Agnès, awkwardly.

"There isn't time," said Anne, walking off. "We must get back for dinner." Agnès covered her face as she passed by the men on her way back to the tower. Hoisting up the skirts of her silky blue gown, she hurried down the steps and set off along the cold, dark passageway, hoping that she wouldn't be late.

8

The clock struck five as Agnès and Anne stepped into the Great Hall. Its walls were aglow from the blaze of a log fire that burned in an enormous hearth. A broad tapestry of forest creatures reached along the back wall. Across the room, between the windows, was a painting of a smiling lady. She was sitting in front of a mural of lakes and jagged mountains with her hands resting on the arm of a chair. Her hair was long and veiled. Soft curls twisted down. Her face was very fair and she seemed to be looking right at Agnès.

"Come and join us," said the Master. "Dinner is almost ready." He was sitting at the head of a long table with his young artist friend. No sooner had Agnès sat down than the housekeeper walked in carrying a large platter.

"I hope you like roast goose," she said, "and vegetables."

"Let me introduce you to Melzi," said the Birdman, turning to his artist friend. The young man was tall and slim. He had auburn hair and eyes of the clearest blue. His slender nose and thin brow gave him a look of nobility, Agnès thought. She smiled and nodded.

"Maturina is my housekeeper," said the Birdman, gesturing

to the plump-faced woman serving dishes. "She has been at Le Cloux the longest."

"Where are the children?" asked Agnès.

"You mean Prince François and Princess Charlotte?" said Maturina, carving off a slice of goose and loading it onto her plate. "They only come when King François goes hunting."

"Why here?"

"The manor house is the King's childhood home," said Maturina. "It's where he grew up as a boy with his mother and sister." She ladled out steaming vegetables and passed around the sauce.

"You must be very rich," said Agnès. "Living in the King's house, I mean." The Birdman shook his head.

"Far from it," he said. "I merely paint and invent things for King François, and in return he lets me stay here."

Reaching for a knife, Agnès cut herself a crust of bread. Glancing along the table, she noticed that the Birdman's plate had been served up with little more than a few roasted carrots, chestnuts and beans.

"Isn't he hungry?" she said, turning to Melzi.

"The Master never eats meat," explained the young artist. "He says that one day, all men will consider the killing of animals wasteful and barbaric."

"And what do you say?" said Agnès. Melzi merely shrugged and carved himself another slice of goose.

"How is your painting coming on?" asked Agnès, trying to

make polite conversation.

"I've almost finished," said Melzi, "It's for a royal celebration next Saturday."

"The Master is planning a grand banquet here at Le Cloux to mark the Prince's baptism," said Maturina. "He has invited guests from all over the kingdom and has lots of surprises in store." Agnès asked if the painting was one of those surprises, but Melzi said that the King and Queen already knew about it. They had commissioned it in honour of the Dauphin Prince and his sister, Princess Charlotte.

"So what are the surprises?" Agnès asked. The Birdman looked over.

"That would be telling," he said, tapping the side of his nose.

"Where will you go when you leave us?" Maturina asked.

"I live alone," said Agnès.

"You mean there's no one to take care of you?" said the housekeeper.

"Well, there is Magellan," said Agnès. "But he's just a crow and he isn't much help."

"What about your parents?" said Maturina. Agnès went on to explain that her mother had died when she was young and that her father had gone away. She recalled arriving in Amboise, one chilly night, aboard his little rowing boat. She spoke of seeing the lights of the Royal Château for the first time, shimmering on the Loire. She remembered the smell of

Sister Celeste's oil lamp as she greeted them at the convent door.

"My papa left me at the Minimes Convent," she said. "But he promised to come back."

"Where did he go?" asked Maturina, dishing out more carrots.

"Across the sea," said Agnès, "to seek his fortune."

"How long has he been gone?" asked Melzi.

"Four years," said Agnès. "I was eight when he left."

"But if he left you at the convent," said Maturina, "why do you live alone?"

"Because I ran away," said Agnès. Maturina put down her fork.

"Stay here with us," she said. "I can make up a remedy for those bruises and have you well again in no time."

"I've troubled you enough," said Agnès. The Master dabbed his mouth with a napkin.

"Nonsense," he said. "You have been no bother at all." Agnès thought for a while.

"I suppose Magellan could manage without me," she said. "He does need to fend for himself more."

"That settles it," said the Master, turning to Maturina. "Holly bark and elm leaves are best for the bruising, and comfrey root is perfect for mending bones."

When the meal was over, and everyone had helped to clear away the dishes, Agnès climbed the stairs to her room. Putting on a clean nightgown, she sat on the bed and stared at her reflection in the looking glass. Light from an oil lamp played on its surface. How thin and wretched she looked. She thought about the other girls her own age back at the convent, with their fair complexions and silky hair. Hers was nothing but a fly-away tangle that, no matter how hard she tried to tame, would twist and twine with a wilfulness of its own.

When Maturina came in, she was carrying a tray with three steaming dishes on it. She set it down by the bedside. Picking up a small bowl and a spoon, she reached over.

"Drink this," she said.

"Is it one of the Master's potions?" asked Agnès. Maturina nodded.

"The very best," she said. "The Master says comfrey root is one of Nature's finest remedies." Agnès sipped from the edge of the spoon.

"Yack!" she spluttered, spitting the stuff out.

"It only works on the inside," said Maturina. Agnès held her nose and took another mouthful. When the bowl was empty, Maturina dipped a cloth in a bowl of murky brown liquid and placed it on Agnès's leg. Agnès could feel the warmth seeping into her bones.

"What's that?" she asked.

"Holly bark and elm leaves," said Maturina. "The Master recommends it for bruises." She dipped a clean towel in warm water and mopped Agnès's face.

"You only have to be my guardian until I'm well again," said Agnès.

"I know," said Maturina, "That's why you must get all the rest you can." She wrung the cloth out and dabbed her forehead. "After you left the convent, where did you go?" she asked.

"I went to live in one of the Troglodyte caves."

"Alone?"

"I have Magellan to keep me company," said Agnès. "Though sometimes I don't see him for days." She told the housekeeper about the time she found him as a tiny chick, chirping at the foot of a tree. She had fed him worms and insects until he was strong enough to fly. She recalled the day he spread his wings for the first time and leapt from her outstretched hands, taking to the air in flight.

"He just knew what to do," she said.

Agnès went on to tell Maturina all about the sisters of the Minimes Convent who had taken care of her since that first night when Sister Celeste opened the convent door. She spoke of Sister Flora who taught her the names of flowers, plants and trees; Sister Celeste who knew about the stars in the night sky; Sister Eunice who showed her how to spin and sew; and Brother Herwald who taught her to read and write.

"It sounds wonderful," said Maturina. "Why ever did you leave?"

"Haven't you ever felt trapped?" said Agnès. "Doesn't this

place seem like a prison to you?" Maturina shook her head.

"Not at all," she replied. "I can come and go as I please."

"Well, I felt trapped," said Agnès. Like a bird that is meant to fly free, she had always known that one day she would leave the convent. When the time came for her to fly away, it seemed like the right thing to do. Like Magellan, she could feel the air breathing through her feathers.

Agnès recalled how, early one morning, before the sun was up, she got dressed and wrapped Mother Mary in a muslin cloth. Creeping down the stairs from her attic room, she had slipped on a plain grey cloak. Sister Honorine was on her knees, wheezing softly in the hallway. Agnès tiptoed past, taking care not to wake her up. She slipped through the back door and eased it shut. She made her way over to where the garden wall had fallen into disrepair, and foxes got in at night. Squeezing through the narrow gap, she made her escape.

Agnès told Maturina about all the wonderful things she had done and the people she had met since then. She spoke of the Romani folk who taught her to sing and dance by their camp-fires, the falconers who showed her their hunting birds, and the woodsmen who taught her about forest creatures. Sometimes she would walk along the riverbank, stopping to hear the boatmen tell tales of far-off lands. When the sun was high, she would climb the hill and—like an eagle in its lofty nest—survey the comings and goings of the people below. All the while Agnès would be watching and waiting for her papa to come home.

"I'm sure your father will return one day," said Maturina.

"If he doesn't, I'll go looking for him," said Agnès. "I'll search across the sea until I find him."

"Then you must rest," said Maturina. "For a journey like that, you will need to be strong." Tucking in the covers, she picked up her tray of dishes and snuffed out the candle.

Agnès nestled beneath her cocoon of soft bedsheets. She felt her aches and pains slowly melt away. As she closed her eyes, a warm feeling came over her. She sensed in some strange way that the Manor of Le Cloux was where the Fates wanted her to be.

9

Rain drizzled down the window panes and puddled on the narrow ledge outside Agnès's room. Along with the steady drip-drop, she could hear the plink of strings being played in some far-off corner of the manor house. Wrapping a shawl around her, she made her way down the twisting stairway to the lobby below. With each step, the musical incantation grew louder, leading her on until she came to the salon. Turning the handle, Agnès pushed open the door and looked inside.

The Birdman was sitting on a stool with a lyre balanced on his knee. It was like a harp, carved on top with a horse's head. He was plucking the strings with one hand and brushing down on them with the other. When he had finished playing, Agnès closed the door.

"You like music?" said the Birdman, looking around. Agnès nodded.

"What sort do you prefer?"

"I like to hear the Romani people play," said Agnès. The old man put down his lyre. He walked over to the window and gazed out at the shifting rain clouds.

"Music is like sunshine," he said. "It turns dull days into summertime."

"I expect that's why the birds sing," said Agnès. The Birdman poked at a web in the corner of the window and watched the spider dance.

"Have you ever wondered how birds learn to sing and spiders know how to spin?" he said. "Do they learn from other birds and spiders, or are they born knowing what to do?"

"I think they probably hear the music," said Agnès.

"What music is that?" said the Birdman.

"The music inside them," said Agnès. "Haven't you heard it?" The Birdman smiled.

"Yes, I hear it all the time," he said, gazing wistfully out of the window.

"Where do you suppose all the birds go in the wintertime?" he asked.

"I expect they fly away to other lands, then come back when it warms up again," said Agnès. The Birdman scratched his head.

"Some say they sleep in the mud—others say they turn into stone eggs that hatch out again in the springtime."

"That can't be true," said Agnès.

"No, I'm sure you're right," said the Birdman. "I never did believe all that other nonsense."

In the corner of the room was a curious cabinet with its lid propped open. Agnès went over to it. Like an organ, the cabinet had keys and pedals. It also had strings, like a harp, with wheels underneath them.

"What is this thing?" she asked.

"I call it the viola organista," said the Birdman. He fetched a stool and sat down. Pressing the pedals with his feet, he ran his fingers over the keys. Wheels whirred, strings vibrated, and the room was filled with the sound of violins. Agnès closed her eyes and listened.

"This must be what heaven sounds like," she said softly. When the Birdman stopped playing, she opened her eyes. "Did you invent it yourself?" she asked.

"Yes, but it needs a few adjustments," said the Birdman. "The wheels are rather stiff."

"I suppose that's a job for another day, like the flying machine," said Agnès. The Birdman sighed.

"I have so much to do and so little time to do it," he lamented.

He picked up his horse-head lyre and strummed it gently. As he played, Agnès plucked up the courage to ask a question of her own.

"Why did you buy the little songbird and set it free?" she said.

"You saw me do that?" said the Birdman. Agnès gave a nod.

"A few sous is a small price to pay for freedom," said the Birdman.

"Then, why not buy all the birds? You have enough money don't you?"

"You think I haven't tried? If I buy them all, the old woman will only go out and catch more."

"How do you decide which ones to set free?" Agnès asked.

"Some birds are very pretty and are sure to be given a good home," explained the Birdman. "Others are so scrawny that no one ever wants to buy them—those are the ones I choose."

Agnès thought about all the books she had seen in the upstairs library.

"I've been looking at your bird drawings," she said. "I hope you don't mind." The Birdman put down his lyre.

"Not at all," he said. "They were never meant to be hidden away." Agnès asked how he was able to make them look so real. "I draw what I see and feel," said the Birdman. "It's like hearing the music you were talking about."

After more of Maturina's potions and stew, Agnès climbed the stairs to the Birdman's study. She reached down a book from the cabinet and sat by the window in a big comfy chair. Looking out, she watched as the shifting clouds stretched and pulled apart. Patches of blue started to appear and slowly grew into one bright expanse. Rays of sunlight reached in through the windows, lighting up the pages of the book on her lap. Agnès leafed through drawings of ferocious creatures that the Birdman had drawn. There were dragons, demons, monsters and leviathans. Beside each one, he had jotted things down. Agnès tried to read what he had put, but she couldn't understand a single word. In all her years at the convent, she had never seen such an alphabet. She had been taught to read French and Latin by Brother Herwald, but this was something entirely different. The shapes of the letters were unlike any she had seen before.

Reaching down a collection of loose pages, bound together in a folio, Agnès looked through detailed drawings of body parts. Arms, legs and torsos were all depicted with lines running through them, like the roots and branches of a tree. There was even a drawing of an unborn infant, curled up small like a baby chick inside an egg.

Amongst the Birdman's books, Agnès found one full of cannons and ballistae. One such war machine was an enormous catapult. The giant crossbow had wheels and was pulled by heavy horses. It looked as if it could knock down the walls of a castle, and had huge winding mechanisms for pulling back on the arms.

Agnès was amazed by the Master's skill and artistry. With ink and chalk, and the finest of shaded lines, he could conjure up all sorts of wonderful and terrible things. All day long, she sat nestled in her chair by the window, lost in a world of books.

10

A cool stillness descended over the Manor of Le Cloux. When an owl hooted, Agnès got up from her chair and leaned out of the window. She could see the watchman lighting coloured lanterns. Glimmering orbs of red, yellow and blue illuminated the courtyard and the pathway below. The Birdman stepped out, wrapped in a long fur cloak. Rubbing his hands, he walked briskly, following the trail of lanterns.

Fetching her mantle from the closet, Agnès descended the stairs to the lobby. She opened the manor house door and stepped out into the night. The air felt cool. With her hood up and her hands deep in her pockets, she followed the coloured lights along the path. Moonlight gleamed through the trees, and shifting clouds swelled like foamy waves in the night sky. Crossing over the wooden bridge, she heard another owl hoot and the plop of a toad in the water.

When she got to the Birdman's red-brick workshop, Agnès could see a misty glow rising from the chimney. Creeping up to the barn doors, she peered in through the gap between them.

Oil lamps burned brightly inside the barn, casting long shadows that reached across the workshop floor. A mouse scampered amongst the sawdust and wood shavings. The Birdman was wearing his leather apron and was holding a bundle of rags. Going over to one of the workbenches, he pulled back a large canvas cover. Agnès leaned in for a better view. As the gap between the doors widened, she saw a large silver swan, sitting on the workbench. Its eyes glinted like diamonds and its slender neck reached up in a graceful curve. The Birdman set to work, rubbing the swan's metallic back with a rag. As he polished, the swan made little clinking noises.

When Agnès leaned in further, the door's iron latch slammed down with a loud clank. The Birdman looked around.

"Who's there?" he called out.

"It's me," said Agnès rather awkwardly. She opened the door wide and stepped into the barn.

"So, my secret is out," said the Birdman. "You have discovered the Cigno."

"I'm sorry—I didn't mean to intrude, said Agnès." The Birdman beckoned her over.

"Come in and have a proper look," he said. Agnès went across to the workbench and gazed at the silver swan. Close up, it was more beautiful than ever. Each feather had been etched with intricate lines.

"It's magnificent," she said. "But can it swim and fly like a real swan?"

"Wait and see," said the Birdman. "I intend to demonstrate

65

at the banquet on Saturday."

"But I won't be there," said Agnès.

"Do you want to be?" asked the Birdman. Agnès shrugged.

"I've never been to a banquet before," she said. "I wouldn't know what to do or say."

"You wouldn't have to do or say anything," said the Birdman. "Leave all that up to me."

"But how would I get an invite?" The Birdman smiled.

"As the Master of Le Cloux, I can invite whoever I wish," he said.

"Are you sure the King wouldn't mind?" said Agnès.

"Of course not," said the Birdman, folding up his rag. "And it would be a great shame if you missed seeing the Cigno take flight."

Agnès picked up a rag and helped to polish the swan's silver feathers. As she worked, she kept glancing up at the Falco, hanging from the rafters above.

"When will the flying machine be ready?" she asked.

"I wish I could say," said the Birdman. "King François is keen for me to finish it—I promised him I would." Agnès gazed along the sleek lines and curves of the Falco's wings.

"What is there still to do?"

"Well, there are braces to add, control wires to be fitted, and the wings need stitching."

"How long will all that take?" said Agnès. The Birdman

thought for a moment.

"Weeks—perhaps months," he said.

"Can I help?" Agnès asked. The Birdman shook his head and said that the task of building the Falco was for him alone to complete.

"I'm very fussy," he said. "One single mistake could spell disaster." Agnès didn't say anything, but the Birdman must have seen the look of disappointment in her eyes. "Actually there is an important job you can help with," he went on. "Be in the courtyard tomorrow morning at eight and I'll explain all about it."

By the time the swan was done, Agnès was starting to feel weary. She helped the Birdman pack away his things before setting off back to the manor house.

"Don't be late," he said as she walked off. "Remember to be in the courtyard at eight o'clock prompt."

On her way back to the house, Agnès stopped on the wooden bridge by the stream. She pulled up her hood as a cool chill blew through the trees and stirred the water below. Hearing the crunch of footsteps, she looked along the trail of lights and saw a dark figure heading along the path towards her. It was Monsieur Hugo.

"You!" said the watchman, holding out his lantern. "Why are you sneaking around down here?" Agnès shook her head.

"I wasn't sneaking—I came out for some fresh air."

"Well, you shouldn't be down here—not at this late hour."
The watchman's hound sniffed and snorted.

Grabbing Agnès by the arm, Hugo marched her back along
the path, muttering under his breath as he went.

When they reached the manor house gates, he led her over
to the guardhouse. Throwing the door wide, he bundled her
inside. The little room was dimly lit and sparsely furnished.
It had one small table and a stool. The walls were hung with
weapons of every sort. There were swords, spears, pikes
and maces, as well as a fine crossbow that hung over the fire
mantel. Embers smouldered in the hearth and the place smelt
of sulphur powder.

The watchman poured himself a mug of ale and sat down on his stool. He threw his dog a bone. As the hound settled by the fire and began to gnaw, Agnès stared into the glowing embers. She wondered what this was all about.

"I want the truth," said Hugo. "Who are you?" Agnès didn't say a word. The watchman slurped from his mug.
He looked at her with suspicious eyes.

"Where have I seen you before?" he said. Agnès shrugged.

"In the marketplace," said Hugo, his eyes narrowing. "That's where, isn't it?"

"You must be mistaken," said Agnès. The watchman took another swig from his mug.

"I never forget a face," he said. "And neither does my dog, Nosewise." Agnès glanced over at his hound, slobbering by the fire.

"I told you—I don't know what you mean," she said.

"You might have charmed the old man, but you can't fool me," said Hugo.

Just then, the door swung open and a cool blast swept through the little guardhouse, whipping up the smouldering embers. The Master was standing in the doorway.

"What's going on Hugo?" he said. The watchman sprang to his feet, knocking over his stool.

"I caught her sneaking around," he said. "But it won't happen again."

"I wasn't sneaking," Agnès insisted.

"The young lady can come and go as she pleases," said the Master. Agnès glanced back at the watchman. His eyes were flashing wild.

"But how can we trust her?" he railed. The Master raised himself up.

"Agnès is not a caged bird," he roared, "and I won't have her treated like one."

Hugo was speechless. He stood shaking his head in dismay as the Master turned and stepped back out into the night. Agnès slowly edged her way to the door, then hurried after him.

"Thank you," she said as they walked back across the courtyard together. The Birdman paused by the manor house door.

"I meant every word of it," he said. "You are free to roam as you please—there will be no caged birds under my roof."

As Agnès climbed the stairs to her room, the watchman's querulous threats echoed in her mind. Hugo was on to her for sure. After hanging her cloak in the closet, she climbed into bed. Resting on her mound of soft pillows, she pulled the covers over her head and tried to put the whole thing out of her mind.

11

he room of books was the mind and genius of Le Cloux, but the manor house kitchen was the heart and belly of the place. A fire burned in the hearth and Agnès was greeted by the smell of freshly baked bread as she walked in early the next morning. Fetching a plate and fork, she stood watching Maturina who was boiling a pot of oats on the fire.

Through the window, she could see Melzi, working at his easel in the bright morning light. He was adding a few finishing touches to his painting of the prince and princess.

As she looked at the portrait of young François, Agnès couldn't help but think what a noble life he would lead. He would never go hungry or want for anything. Every privilege and opportunity would be his. She thought how different it would be for the ragged boy she had met at the quayside.

"Why is the Master being so kind to me?" she asked.

Maturina looked around.

"He wants to give you a chance," she said. "Just as he was given a chance."

"What do you mean?" said Agnès.

"Well, he was once much like you."

"Like me?"

"Yes, he didn't grow up with his parents," explained Maturina, tapping the edge of her pot with a ladle. "His mother was a poor peasant girl who couldn't look after him, and his father never had the time." Agnès was surprised to hear it. She expected the Birdman to have led a life of privilege.

"Who took care of him?" she asked. Maturina put a pan of eggs on the fire. She explained that the Master had been raised by his grandparents.

"When he was your age, he was taken on by a great artist called Verrocchio," she went on to say.

"And that's who gave him a chance?"

"Yes, even though the Master was sometimes in trouble with the town Marshal, Verrocchio always believed in him and taught him to paint and create wonderful things."

"Why was he in trouble with the Marshal?" asked Agnès, somewhat surprised.

"It was many years ago," said Maturina. "I don't suppose anyone remembers now."

Agnès thought about the painting between the windows in the Great Hall—the picture of the lady with long curls, sitting in front of a mural of mountains and lakes.

"Did he paint the smiling lady?" she said. Maturina nodded.

"Her name is Lisa," she said, dishing out a serving of oats and eggs onto Agnès's plate. "She was the wife of a rich merchant back in Tuscany where he used to live."

Agnès sat at the table to eat her breakfast. She peered out through the window at Melzi who was packing away his easel and stowing his paints and brushes in a box. She hoped he wouldn't glance around and see her watching.

"I have to be in the courtyard by eight," she said, finishing off her breakfast and clearing away her plate. "The Master needs help with an important job."

"Then you'll need to wear old clothes," said Maturina. "There are some in a barrel down in the cellar."

Agnès stepped into the courtyard, a short while later, with her sleeves rolled up and her fly-away hair tied back. She had on a baggy shirt and a pair of patched-up hose. When Melzi came along, he was carrying two small pails. He set them down on the edge of the courtyard. Agnès went over. She could see they were full of red and yellow paint.

"What are we painting?" she said. Melzi looked up.

"You'll find out soon enough," he said. "Until then, you can help me carry the rest of these." Agnès followed Melzi over to a small storeroom beside the woodshed. She went back and forth with more buckets of paint, as well as boxes and baskets of brushes, chalks and charcoal. When she was done, she sat on the edge of the water trough to rest. A pleasant smell of wood smoke hung in the air, and the sun felt warm on the back of her neck.

Opening wide the manor house gates, Hugo let in a whole group of people that were chatting and laughing like old friends. Agnès had never seen any of them before. When the Master came out, he stood on the manor house steps, looking out over the little gathering. Clearing his throat, he addressed them all like a captain commanding his troops.

"In a few days, we shall be hosting a royal banquet for the King and Queen, right here at Le Cloux. Your task is to paint a large mural of birds on sheets of silk that will be hung from a scaffold in the courtyard." Agnès gave Melzi a nudge.

"So that's what we're painting," she said.

"Shhh!" said Melzi, teasing apart the bristles of his brush.

The Birdman continued his speech.

"When the King and Queen enter through the manor house gates, they will see your large mural of painted birds, illuminated by a thousand candles. I want to see their faces light up just as brightly. Your efforts must be of the highest order." Everyone was keen to make a start. They began to chatter amongst themselves about how it was to be done.

Before long, huge sheets of silky blue fabric were being rolled out across the courtyard. The fabric was then weighted down with stones, along its edges, to stop it from blowing about. Melzi went around distributing drawing materials and paints amongst the artists. He handed Agnès a stick of chalk to draw with.

"Keep your hand steady," he said, "and don't be too stiff about it."

"I know how to draw birds," said Agnès, somewhat irritably. With broad strokes, she sketched the outline of an enormous stork. Its wings reached out to the edges of the fabric. Melzi looked on and nodded his approval.

"Ben fatto!" he said when she had finished. "You draw well." Dipping her brush into a bucket of white paint, Agnès filled in the bird's wings and tail, adding splashes of orange for its beak and legs.

Melzi got on with a bird of his own. He drew a magnificent peacock and painted it with feathers of purple and red. Agnès kept glancing over as he worked. As the little band of artists sketched and painted, birds of all kinds began to fill the silky blue canvas. The mural quickly took shape. The Birdman paced back and forth—adding a turtle dove here and a chaffinch there—wherever he thought it needed one. On a long trestle, Maturina set out mugs of ale, platters of bread and cheese, and bowls of sweet comfits for the workers.

With her stork completed, Agnès wondered what to draw next. Then it came to her. She would paint the imaginary bird with trailing feathers that she had drawn on the back of the old sea chart and had carved on her prison wall. With broad strokes, she swept her brush across the silky canvas, smoothing and blending its bright plumage of red, yellow and blue. Beneath the bird's wings, she painted smaller birds: swallows, swifts, pipits and finches. From time to time, she would step back to inspect her work.

The little band of artists painted all morning long and late into the afternoon. Beak by beak and feather by feather, the menagerie of fowl grew until the silky blue backdrop was a riot of life and colour. As it neared completion, some of the workers fetched long poles from the barn. They lashed them together to form a high framework from which to hang the mural. Once the scaffold was up, and the painting was ready, they hoisted it high, tying the corners tightly so that they wouldn't flap about in the breeze.

Agnès and Melzi stood admiring the silky blue montage that hung around the courtyard. Gazing up at the spectacle, they marvelled at how the shimmer of silk almost made the birds come alive.

"They look so real," said Agnès. Melzi gave a nod. Laying aside his brushes, he set off up the manor house steps, beckoning to her with a wave of his hand.

"I want you to see something," he called back. Agnès wiped her hands and followed Melzi into the manor house. She found him standing beside a painting of a young man with curly hair. Agnès had walked past the picture many times before but had never stopped for a close look. The young man was holding a wooden cross.

"Who is he?" she asked.

"Saint John the Baptist," said Melzi. Agnès reached out and touched the panel.

"He looks so real," she said. Melzi nodded.

"No one breathes life into a painting the way the Master does," said Melzi.

"How does he do it?" Agnès asked.

"Sfumato," said Melzi.

"I don't understand," said Agnès.

"It's his special way of painting," said Melzi, "with no hard edges." Agnès could see how much Melzi admired his Master's work.

"You are a fine artist too," she said. "You really are."

"Thank you," said Melzi. "One day I hope to return to Milan and set up a painting school of my own."

"You must—it will be a very fine school," said Agnès.

Melzi reached into his pocket and took out an envelope. He handed it to Agnès.

"The Master retired early," he said. "He asked me to give

you this." Agnès opened the envelope and took out a piece of paper. She held it up to the light. Beneath the royal seal of the white salamander was a neatly-penned invitation to the banquet. She read it out loud.

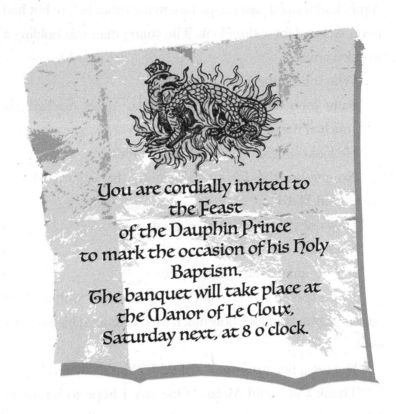

You are cordially invited to
the Feast
of the Dauphin Prince
to mark the occasion of his Holy
Baptism.
The banquet will take place at
the Manor of Le Cloux,
Saturday next, at 8 o'clock.

Agnès folded up her invite and tucked it in the waistband of her hose.

"Tell the Master I accept," she said. "I wouldn't miss it for the world."

12

All week long, Agnès helped to prepare for the feast. She peeled and sliced vegetables, collected eggs, and kneaded dough. She carried plates and cutlery into the Great Hall, where maids and scullions from the Château had set out extra tables. Each afternoon, after her work in the kitchen was done, she would visit the Birdman in his little factory.

One time, he was busy packing the silver swan into a straw-filled crate, ready to be carried over to the manor house. Another time, he had a pile of papers on his workbench. They had been cut into squares and the Birdman said it was all part of his big surprise. Taking a sheet from the pile, he folded it from corner to corner. Opening it out, he then folded it back the other way. After several more folds, he had what looked like a little paper bird. Holding it up, he pulled the bird's tail and its wings flapped.

"That's amazing," said Agnès. "How did you learn to do that?"

"I once knew a man from China who could make all manner of creatures from squares of paper," said the Birdman.

"Let me try," said Agnès, taking a sheet from the pile. As

the Birdman folded, she watched and copied. Her first attempt was a bit clumsy and the bird's wings wouldn't flap properly. Her next attempt was much better. When she tugged the tail, the bird flapped perfectly.

"You learn fast," said the Birdman, dividing up the stack of paper squares. "Now help me fold all these—we need lots more for my surprise." Facing one another across the workbench, Agnès and the Birdman worked all afternoon, making enough paper birds to fill a large basket.

With the simplest of things, the Birdman could fashion the cleverest of creations. He was always busy mending something old or making something new. In his pocket, he carried a notebook and would often stop what he was doing to write down his ideas.

"You must be a master at the art of copying Nature's forms," he said one day as he sat in the garden, watching and drawing a lizard that was sitting on a rock. "You will not be able to do this until you know them by heart." That was his secret. He knew the world by heart and was never too busy to stop and marvel at its wonders.

On the day of the banquet, Agnès went for one last look at the Great Hall. Bunting and greenery had been hung all around, and each table was adorned with fresh lilies. Two chairs were draped in blue velvet for the King and Queen, and a row of stools had been lined up beside the window for the musicians. Despite feeling excited about the whole affair, the thought of mingling with rich and noble guests scared Agnès to death. She hoped that no one would talk to her or ask her any questions.

Climbing the stairs to her chamber, she went off to get ready. Pouring warm water into a bowl, she got up a soapy lather and scrubbed her neck and face. As she rinsed away the suds, she heard a knock on the door. The handle turned and Anne walked in carrying a large bundle in her arms.

"I have the perfect dress for you to wear," she said, holding up a long green gown. "It belongs to Queen Claude."

The dress hung in deep folds of shimmering silk, edged with velvet. Its scalloped sleeves were threaded with ribbons.

With Anne's help, Agnès slipped it on. She gazed at her reflection in the mirror as the maid laced up each arm.

"It fits perfectly," said Anne. "You must be the same size as Queen Claude—at least when she's not great with child." She held out a pair of embroidered slippers. Agnès perched on the edge of the bed and put them on. Stepping lightly, she whirled around the room, letting the folds of her dress float free.

"You look beautiful," said Anne. As she stared at her reflection in the mirror, Agnès could hardly believe her eyes.

"Is that really me?" she said. Anne smiled as she combed and twisted ribbons through Agnès's hair.

"The sisters at the convent always cut my hair short," said Agnès. "They liked it better that way."

"How do you prefer it?" asked Anne. Agnès gazed in the mirror.

"Like this," she said.

"You'll love it at the banquet," said Anne.

"What should I expect?" said Agnès.

"Expect wonderful food, but don't take too much of the wine," said Anne. Hitching up the skirts of her gown, Agnès whirled around the room. Turning back to face the mirror, she stopped and curtsied.

"What if the King speaks to me—what shall I call him?"

"Call him *Your Christian Majesty*," said Anne. "Offer him

your right hand and curtsy only once."

"What about the Queen?"

"The first time you speak to her, you must call her *Your Highness*. After that, just call her Madame."

"What if I forget?"

"Don't worry. No one will lock you in the tower for getting it wrong."

"I suppose not," said Agnès, a little nervously.

While hanging up her old grey mantle, Agnès felt in the pocket. Hidden in the lining was the ruby cloak pin she had stolen from the big nobleman. She took it out. It was a perfect match for the green and gold of her dress.

"What's that?" Anne asked, noticing the pin glinting in the light.

"Nothing!" said Agnès. She quickly hid the jewel away. Anne walked over.

"Let me see," she insisted. Agnès held out her hand and unfurled her fingers.

"What a beautiful gem," said Anne. "Where did you get it?" Agnès struggled to know what to say.

"It's mine," she said at last. "It was my mama's—she gave it to me before she died." Anne took the jewel and held it up.

"Then you must wear it for the banquet," she said, "in memory of your dear departed mother."

"Yes of course," said Agnès, smiling weakly as Anne pinned it to her dress.

13

All around the courtyard, candles burned brightly and lanterns blazed like fiery sentinels. From her upstairs window, Agnès could see courtiers lined up like soldiers on parade. When a trumpet sounded, she hurried downstairs and stood by the door to watch as Monsieur Hugo opened the gates of Le Cloux and the first guests began to arrive. Hooves clattered and carriages jolted to a halt. As the guests stepped out in all their finery and made their way across the courtyard, the Master offered his hand to each one in turn. He had on a scarlet tunic, trimmed with gold, and a matching velvet cap. The Chief Steward unfurled a long parchment and announced each guest as they walked through the doors.

Duke Antoine of Lorraine and his wife Renée.
The Castellan of Amboise
Magister Spirito Fieri of Saint-Denis
Monsieur Guglielmo Borean
Charles and Marguerite of Alençon

There were barons and baronesses, lords and ladies, dukes and magistrates. Agnès watched as a magnificent blue and gold coach passed through the gates and came to a halt right by the manor house steps. The driver climbed down and opened the carriage door. She looked on with eager anticipation as King François and Queen Claude emerged from their royal coach, stopping on their way out to admire the mural of painted birds.

"What beautiful creatures," said the Queen, her eyes lighting up. "One half expects them to fly." Agnès curtsied politely as the King and Queen walked past and climbed the manor house steps. Queen Claude was indeed great with child, just as Anne had said.

In the dining hall, extra tables had been set out ready to receive Maturina's sumptuous feast. Pages stood by with steaming dishes. Scullions scurried back and forth as the Master escorted the King and Queen to their seats beside the Duke and Duchess of Bourbon. Agnès was seated with Melzi and Anne on either side of her.

With everyone in place, the Master got to his feet. He raised his goblet and paid homage to His Most Christian Majesty. After a few words to mark the christening of the young Dauphin Prince, he tugged aside a purple drape, unveiling Melzi's painting of the Prince and Princess. The King and Queen gazed at the picture and agreed that it was a striking likeness. Melzi bowed graciously and everyone applauded.

When the ovation had died away, the Birdman reached up and pulled on a long cord that hung down. A curtain drew back, revealing his magnificent silver swan, hanging from the roof timbers. With feathers of flashing silver, and eyes of glittering crystal, the majestic bird glinted and sparkled in the light. Suspended from a long wire that ran the length of the room, it hung with its broad wings reaching out over the fire mantel.

A bell chimed and everyone looked up with eager anticipation to see what would happen next. Clicking and whirring, the swan began to move. Like giant bellows, it breathed in and out. On beating wings it glided gracefully over the heads of the seated guests. When the swan reached the King and Queen, a bell chimed and the belly of the bird opened wide. Like sparks from an exploding firework, tiny paper birds flew out in all directions. The Great Hall erupted with gasps of astonishment. The King rose from his seat and roared with delight as paper birds showered down on him. Others now leapt to their feet and applauded the Master's genius and the King's great wit.

With the unveiling of Melzi's painting, and the flight of the silver swan a resounding success, minstrels struck up on lutes, pipes and tabors. Servants swept in carrying steaming dishes, lifting their lids to reveal every sort of gamebird: partridge, quail, pheasant, peafowl, grouse, wood-pigeon and snipe—all steeped in sauces of almond, saffron, honey and ginger. The Birdman was served little more than a few roasted carrots, chestnuts and beans.

Agnès made a start on the enormous platter of food that had been set before her. As she ate, she did her best to catch something of the conversation going on. The Duke of Bourbon spoke of his triumphal victory at the battle of Marignano. He boasted of thirty brave charges and seventy-two cannons that had broken through the Swiss lines.

"A true battle of giants," said the Duke. "All other battles have been merely sport by comparison."

Duke Antoine spoke of the rise of the wretched Protestants in the North, as he put it. He complained about the revolt of the peasant farmers. King François seemed less concerned with such matters and preferred to talk of Spanish and Portuguese ships returning from the Americas with reports of explorations in that strange New World.

"I must send a ship or two over there to see what all the fuss is about," said the King, picking at the food on his plate.

"If you want my mind, we should rid ourselves of every devil-tongued Protestant," railed Duke Antoine, pulling at his beard. "I say we banish the lot of them to the Americas."

"A waste of good shipping, my dear man," said a weasel-faced fellow sitting across the table. Agnès was about to speak up when she remembered what the Birdman had said about holding her tongue.

Ladies gossiped in tight huddles. Men snorted in bawdy laughter at one another's quips.

During the evening, Agnès kept noticing Queen Claude glancing over. She felt awkward knowing that she was wearing one of her dresses. She also grew aware of a large man seated across the hall. Like the Queen, he had been watching her for quite some time. Whenever Agnès looked at him, the man quickly turned away.

"What do you think of the minstrels?" said the Birdman, pointing his fork at the ensemble of players over by the window.

"Are they Protestants?" barked Duke Antoine, his mouth full of grouse. The Birdman tapped his fork irritably on the edge of his plate and leaned in.

"I trust that the Duke's enjoyment of music is not spoilt by his taste in religion," he said. "In fact, I have heard many a fine tune plucked out by a Muslim and a Jew, as well as a Catholic and a Protestant." The Duke raised an eyebrow.

"An interesting observation," he said, drumming his fingers on the table in time to the music. Agnès tugged at the Birdman's sleeve.

"I think they play wonderfully," she said in a low whisper. "Just like the Romani people," said the Birdman, giving a nod.

No sooner had scullions cleared away all the empty dishes, than others came in with plates of sweets and dragées. The

Birdman seemed to favour anise comfits. Agnès noticed his face light up when a whole plate of them was served. Another dish was piled high with spiced pastries.

"What are they?" she asked.

"Turkish hats," said Anne. "They are full of sweet cheese." Agnès had never known luxuries quite like it. Wearing the Queen's dress and mixing with royals and nobles had opened up a whole new world to her.

The hour grew late and the clock chimed. In dribs and drabs, guests began to leave the Great Hall for their waiting carriages. After finishing off one last pastry, Agnès went around picking up all the little paper birds that littered the floor. She noticed a whole pile of them over by the fireplace. Sweeping up a handful, she began tossing them into the smouldering embers. The little birds quickly turned brown and burst into flames, vanishing up the chimney like fiery spirits.

When Agnès turned around, the big nobleman who had been watching her earlier on was standing right in front of her. He took off his hat. Looking up into his beady eyes, and seeing his shiny bald head, she suddenly let out a gasp.

"Do I know you?" said the man, puffing out his chest and tight-buttoned doublet. Agnès froze.

"I am quite sure of it," insisted the nobleman, staring. He pointed at the red ruby, fastened to her dress. Instinctively, Agnès clasped a hand over the jewel.

"Isn't that my pin?" blurted the man. Agnès shook her

head.

"No, it's mine," she said.

"But there isn't another one like it," said the nobleman. "It's one of a kind." Agnès didn't know what to say.

"We have a rascal in our midst," called out the nobleman, pointing. "A brigand and a thief, no less." Heads turned. Agnès made a sudden bolt for the door. She bumped headlong into a scullion, sending his tray of empty dishes flying. She barged into a lady and knocked a goblet from her hand. Wine spilt everywhere.

"Stop her—she's a thief!" called out the bald nobleman.

Agnès ran out into the courtyard. She swept past a huddle of guests who were waiting by their carriages, scattering them in every direction. Like a fleeting spirit, she fled through the manor house gates, vanishing into the night.

With her heart pounding and her head spinning, Agnès stumbled along. Her side ached terribly. When she came to a narrow path that led over the hill to the Château, her feet slowed to a steady plod. The way grew steep. As she clambered up the hill in the cold and dark, spots of rain began to splash down and the path turned slippery and treacherous. Tormented by the pain in her side, she stopped to catch her breath. A ghostly white spectre flew off over the trees, hooting as it went.

As she climbed the muddy hillside, the rain ran in rivulets all around. When the hem of her dress caught on a thicket, Agnès cursed and tore it free. She pressed on, her feet trailing through the mud and mire—convinced that the whole world was conspiring to bring about her ruin. "Even the trees and the rocks are in on it," she told herself.

Cold and shivering, Agnès came to the familiar rills and ridges of her cavern hideaway. By the time she reached the entrance, all her strength was gone. It was about all she could do to cast aside her shoes and drag off the Queen's clinging dress. Flopping down on her bed of dry straw, she lay with her face buried in her arms, sobbing as the rain outside sleeted and the wind howled.

14

Agnès woke up to the sound of tapping and clanking, ringing in her ears. Sitting up, and rubbing her eyes, she saw Magellan, perched on the lid of the old sea chest, pecking at the lock with his beak.

"Oh it's you," she said, brushing straw from her hair and face. When Magellan hopped down and cawed loudly, Agnès went over and prised open the chest lid.

"There's not much left," she said, peering inside and fishing out a few scraps of stale bread and cheese.

"Help yourself," she said, scattering bits of maggot-infested crumbs on the cavern floor for Magellan to pick through.

At the bottom of the chest was a ragged old kirtle. Agnès took it out. She gave it a shake and put it on. It was the one she had been wearing the day she ran away from the convent. The kirtle felt tight and itchy. She lit a candle and placed it in the rocky niche beside Mother Mary.

"Not even you will think kindly of me," she said. "I'm a thief and an intruder, and look at what I've done to the Queen's dress." She picked up the wet, crumpled heap from the cavern floor. It was torn and covered in mud.

"I can't go back to Le Cloux now," muttered Agnès. "Everyone knows I'm a thief." She poked at holes in the dress and twisted frayed ribbon around her finger. The candle flickered and Mother Mary seemed to smile. Agnès recalled the night she was given the little statue. She had been missing her papa terribly and was crying hard. It was all the Reverend Mother could do to comfort her. Now, the statue only reminded her how far she had fallen from grace. Agnès thought about her life at the convent.

"Perhaps it wasn't so bad," she said softly. "At least I was safe there." Magellan cawed. Reaching down, Agnès stroked his silky feathers.

"What shall I do now?" she said, feeling more anxious than ever about showing her face on the streets of Amboise. "What if I go back to the convent for a little while—just until I've worked out what to do next?" Magellan could only nod and flap as she wrestled with the thought that she had finally run out of options.

Knowing that she had little choice, Agnès reached for a knife and began to cut off her hair. Thick clumps tumbled to the cavern floor. Combing and flattening what remained with her fingers, she stared at her pale reflection in the mirror.

"Come and see me in the convent garden," she said. "I'll look out for you there." Stuffing the Queen's dress into the old sea chest, along with the slippers and the red ruby pin, she closed the lid and snuffed out her candle. Wrapping Mother

Mary in a muslin cloth, she went over to the cavern entrance and stepped out into the cool morning air.

Clambering down the hillside, with the statue under her arm, Agnès scrambled over rocks and grassy clumps, descending like a falling leaf to the streets below. At the bottom, she set off for the convent, wondering what she would say when she got there. She stepped aside for a huntsman and his hounds who were coming the other way. The hounds drooled and strained, pulling the fellow along. Continuing on her way, Agnès felt a knot inside tighten. When she saw the convent door up ahead, her footsteps slowed and her stomach began to churn.

"What will the Reverend Mother think of me for running away?" she thought. Clutching Mother Mary tightly, she reached up and knocked. When the door opened, a young sister peered out.

"Can I help you?" asked the sister.

"I'd like to speak with Mother Superior," said Agnès.

"Who shall I say wants to see her?" the sister asked.

"Tell her it's Agnès." The young sister opened the door wide.

"Come in," she said. Agnès stepped across the threshold and waited by the door. She looked up at carved wooden panels of the blessed virtues. As she gazed along the high vaulted passageway, a thousand dark memories came flooding back. She recalled long days, waiting for her papa to return. She remembered countless nights—lying awake, plotting her escape.

The grey walls of the Minimes Convent closed in once more. A familiar spirit seemed to be tugging like a restless hound, straining at its leash—panting and drooling to be off. Agnès knew she didn't belong back at the convent. She was making a big mistake.

Opening the door wide, and with her arm wrapped tightly around Mother Mary, she dashed out into the street. Her only thought was to get away. With her feet flying, and her heart pounding, she ran along the alleyway. In her wild haste, and hardly looking where she was going, she barged headlong into a tall man coming the other way. The man's hat flew from his head and his cane went spinning into the gully. Crashing down on the hard stone cobbles, Agnès threw out her arms. Her little statue slipped from her grasp and rolled off.

"Clumsy child!" snapped the man.

"I'm so sorry," Agnès cried. "I didn't see you." When she looked up, her blood ran chill. Towering over her, glaring down like a ravenous wolf, stood Marshal Lupus, the thief-catcher of Amboise. Like a helpless fawn, Agnès felt trapped.

"What's the hurry?" snapped Lupus. He reached for his hat and straightened his feather. Agnès looked up, trembling. She couldn't speak.

"What were you carrying?" said the Marshal, spotting the muslin bundle in the gutter. He reached down and unwrapped Mother Mary from her shroud.

"Where did you get this?" he said. Agnès shrugged.

"It's mine," she said.

Looking along the alley and seeing the wide-open door of the convent, the Marshal nodded.

"You stole it didn't you?"

"No, you don't understand," Agnès protested.

"I think I understand perfectly well," barked Lupus. "In fact, your face looks familiar. I've seen you before haven't I?" Agnès didn't say a word.

"Urchins like you never own up to their thieving ways," sneered the Marshal. Dragging her up, he marched her off along the thoroughfare.

"Get off me!" yelled Agnès, struggling to pull herself free. An old woman stopped and turned to see what all the fuss was about. Agnès continued to curse and cry out as the Marshal dragged her along. It was no use—Lupus would hear none of it. His grip tightened all the more as he led her off.

At the end of the alley, where the castle wall loomed large, a brown bear in heavy shackles gazed around darkly as Agnès passed by. Her heart ached at the sight of it. She hung her head in shame as Lupus led her past a huddle of onlookers halfway up the castle rampart. When they got to the tower gates, he signalled to the guard. A key rattled in the lock and the gates opened wide. Agnès felt the sharp prod of the Marshal's cane in her back, forcing her through the dark portal. She ducked low as they passed beneath an arch and went down a narrow passage. In the dim light, voices echoed like demons. Dragging her feet, she passed by row upon row of studded doors with heavy iron locks and hinges. Flickering shadows waxed and waned in the lamplight. When they came to a door at the end of the passage, the Marshal took a key from his belt and turned it in the lock. He shoved Agnès inside and slammed the door shut. Agnès stood trembling in the cold and dark. Tears welled up in her eyes. She slumped down on a low stool and sobbed as the Marshal's footsteps ebbed away.

15

Wiping away the tears, Agnès looked around in the gloom of her dismal prison cell. Shafts of light reached in through the narrow bars of a window, high up, painting shadowy stripes along the walls and ceiling. Beneath the window was a hard wooden bed, draped over with a rough blanket. Gouged into the walls, she could see all kinds of birds and beasts. There were bears and boars, eagles and owls. It was clearly the work of some lonely prisoner with nothing but time on his hands. A shiny black beetle scurried up the wall.

Agnès slowly got to her feet. She went over to the wooden bed and stepped up onto it. Peering out through the bars of her cell window, she could see the clouds and the tops of roofs. Sinking back down, she pulled the ragged blanket over her shoulders. A light flickered in the passageway and a face peered in. When the light faded, she curled up in a tight ball. The hours passed slowly. Agnès listened to every noise and stir. Each tap, scratch, creak and moan, kept her awake. When the noises merged into one, and her eyes grew heavy, she slipped into a deep and silent slumber.

Agnès woke up after who-knows-how-long to the sound

of footsteps. She looked and saw a fresh bowl of soup beside her prison door. As she sat on her stool, eating her rations, she looked around at all the birds and animals. Gouged into the crumbling plaster and tufa-stone, they reminded her of the carvings she had seen in the grand salon at the Château. Reaching up, she ran her fingers over their lines and contours. Every creature was a miniature masterpiece, etched with fine lines, like the Birdman's drawings.

Across the way, Agnès could hear someone singing. The tune sounded strangely familiar. When she looked out through her prison door, she could see sad eyes gazing back at her. The eyes blinked.

"Hello," she said. The singing stopped and someone said hello back. When Agnès looked more closely, she could see a scruffy boy.

"Who are you?" she asked. The boy said his name was Pepin. He said that Lupus had caught him with a string of pearly beads, but he hadn't stolen them—a lady had dropped them, and he had picked them up.

"You!" said Agnès. "I know you—I saw you—I was there." She told Pepin her name and said she was sorry he had been caught.

"The Marshal got you too," said Pepin. "I thought you were a good thief." Agnès shook her head.

"There's no such thing as a good thief," she said.

"How did Lupus catch you?"

"I was trying to get away from the convent and didn't see him coming."

"You stole from the convent?"

"No, I didn't steal from the convent," said Agnès irritably.

"But you've stolen things before," said Pepin. "I've seen you do it." Agnès looked along the passageway. The lamp on the wall was burning low.

"What song were you singing just now?" she asked.

"A song that Bertrand taught me," said Pepin.

"Bertrand?"

"He was here before you came," said Pepin.

"Where is he now?" asked Agnès.

"Lupus set him free."

"Why was he in here?"

"I'm not sure," said Pepin. "All I know is, he was a Protestant and some people didn't like what he said." Agnès thought back to the banquet at Le Cloux and all the awful things Duke Antoine had said about the Protestants and their devil-tongued ways.

"What was his song about?" she asked.

"Freedom," said Pepin. Agnès laughed.

"Maybe for Bertrand, but not us," she said.

"But we are all free," Pepin insisted. "Bertrand said so."

"Will you sing me his song?" said Agnès. "I'd like to hear it." Pepin sang out in the darkness like a little songbird, and Agnès hummed along to the half-familiar tune.

My thoughts shall be free, for no one can know them.
They flitter and flee, like shadows in the nighttime.
No archer can shoot them; no hunter can trap them.
And so you can see, my thoughts shall be free.

"Will you teach it to me?" said Agnès, when Pepin had finished. Pepin gave a nod. He recited each line slowly, and together they sang them over and over until the guard came and demanded that they stop. When the guard had gone, Pepin taught Agnès the rest of the words.

I think what I want—whatever excites me,
In the still of the night, my hopes will delight me.
My greatest desire shall burn like a fire.
And so you can see, my thoughts shall be free.

If I should be cast in the darkest of prisons,
No bars could hold back my innermost visions.
For thoughts conquer all and tear down the walls.
And so you can see, my thoughts shall be free.

That night, wrapped in her rough prison blanket, Agnès lay awake with the words to Bertrand's song of hope going round and round in her head. She couldn't get it out of her mind. She decided that, if she was free to think whatever she liked, she would conjure up something other than iron bars and grey walls. As she closed her eyes, fleeting images swirled and formed into half-forgotten shapes and shadows. Like reflections in a looking glass, she saw glimpses of the past. She saw the Birdman and Melzi in the marketplace, setting the little brown linnet free.

The vision faded and, in its place, she saw his room full of books, with the little mechanical bird that sang and flapped. She saw a thousand winged fowl, painted on giant sheets of blue silk. Hanging up in the barn, she saw the Birdman's flying machine, waiting for its moment to fly and fill the whole universe with wonder, just as he dreamt it would.

As she curled up beneath her blanket, Agnès saw herself as the imaginary bird with trailing feathers—the one she had drawn on the old sea chart and had painted on the silky blue mural. In her mind's eye, she stretched out her wings and flew up to the narrow window ledge where the moon and stars shone brightly. She felt the air breathe through her feathers.

Leaping from the precipice, Agnès rose up into the night sky and soared over the rooftops. Climbing higher and higher, she circled the Royal Château and flew past the Minimes Convent. Swooping low over the river, she dipped her tail feathers in the shimmering waters. She beat her magnificent wings and arched high over Amboise, bursting through the clouds to reach for the moon.

16

Nights were long, and the days dragged on. Agnès measured the passing hours by the chime of the church bells and the coming and going of the guards. She hummed tunes and sang songs with Pepin to while away the time. When they tired of singing about ogres and faeries, they would tell one another stories across the passageway. Agnès recounted tales of street urchins being sent down mines to dig for tin and copper—and thieves being taken to distant lands, with no way of ever getting home again.

"My papa went away," said Pepin, "and never came back."

"What happened to him?" asked Agnès.

"He died in the Swiss wars," said Pepin. "They say he was a hero."

"What did he do?"

"Mama said he was very brave and saved someone's life."

"Where is your mother now?"

"In the poor house with the twins, Ida and Eva."

"Why didn't you go with them?"

"I did," said Pepin, "but then I ran away." He spoke about the little cottage where his family used to live. It was down by the Amasse. He said it had white walls and blue shutters, and that he slept in the little attic room at the top. He spoke about his papa, Etienne Moreau, who was sent to fight in a far-off land. After he died, his mother was forced to leave the cottage and take her children to the poorhouse of Saint-Lazarus. Life there had been hard. That's why Pepin ran off. He wanted to help his mama and sisters get their cottage back.

When Pepin had finished, Agnès spoke about the time her father left her at the convent and promised to return but never did.

"That doesn't mean he didn't want to come back for you," said Pepin. "Perhaps he just couldn't." Agnès pressed her face against the bars of her prison door.

"Perhaps you're right?" she said softly.

"Where did your papa go?" asked Pepin.

"To the Americas," said Agnès, "to seek his fortune."

She told Pepin all about her time at Le Cloux—how she had been nursed back to health by Maturina after falling from the manor house wall. She told him about the Birdman and his flying machine, hanging up in the barn.

"Why did you leave?" Pepin asked. "I would have stayed."

"I had no choice," said Agnès. She went on to explain about being caught wearing the nobleman's red ruby at the banquet—about running away and being accused of stealing Mother Mary.

"And did you?" said Pepin. Agnès shook her head.

"I told you, of course not," she said. "Mother Superior gave her to me when I lived at the convent."

"The Marshal was wrong about us both then," said Pepin.

When Agnès heard flapping and tapping, she went over to her window. She climbed up and looked out.

"Magellan, is that you?" she said. It was. He was perched on the ledge, ruffling his feathers and pecking at the bars. Agnès suddenly had a thought. She got down, reached beneath her bed, then climbed back up with something in her hand.

"Have these," she said, holding out a clutch of dead cockroaches that she had squashed in the night. Magellan snatched at the revolting morsels as Agnès told him all about the Birdman and his flying machine.

"It's amazing," she said, "and the Birdman is sure it will fly." Magellan paced back and forth along the ledge, cawing loudly. "I have no more cockroaches," said Agnès. "You've had the lot." Magellan nestled down on the ledge and listened as she sang him songs and told him about her new friend, Pepin.

"He ran away too," she said. "We were both locked up for something we didn't do."

When the wind changed, Magellan turned to face the breeze. He ruffled his feathers and stretched out his wings. With a giant leap, he flapped up to the sky and flew away.

Sitting back down on her low stool, Agnès stared at the wall. She could hear Pepin moving about in his cell. After a while, she got up and went over to the door.

"How long was Bertrand locked up in here?" she asked.

"Four years," said Pepin.

"Four years!" gasped Agnès. "And he never gave up hope?"

"Bertrand said that as long as we have our thoughts we have hope."

"Four years is a long time to sit thinking and hoping," said Agnès. "I would go mad."

"Bertrand was too busy to go mad," said Pepin. "I used to hear him carving things on the walls." In the glimmer of the light, Agnès looked around at all the birds and beasts.

"He did all these?" she said.

"Bertrand was a woodcarver," said Pepin. "He worked at the Château for the King."

"Where did he get tools from, in here?" Agnès asked.

"He made them," said Pepin, "from broken bones. He was carving an eagle the day they set him free." Agnès looked and marvelled at how Bertrand's carving seemed so real, just like the Birdman's drawings.

As she glanced around at the mural of forest creatures, she pictured another bird carved there—her imaginary bird of paradise. She knew the outline and shape by heart. By the time the light had faded, she had it all worked out. Retracing every line and curve in her mind's eye, she pictured it flying alongside Bertrand's majestic eagle.

That evening, Agnès settled down to eat her rations. She

gnawed all the meat from her pig's trotter, then struck it against the floor several times until a sharp piece broke off. A light flickered out in the passageway. It was enough for her to see what she was doing, so she made a start. Reaching up to the wall, she began to scrape and gouge at the loose cement with her sliver of broken bone. It didn't take long to carve out her first line. Slowly and steadily, she etched the shape of the bird with trailing tail feathers into the soft tufa-stone. All evening long, she scratched and carved until it was finished. As she sat back to admire her work, she heard footsteps approaching. The light grew brighter and a guard peered in.

"Get to sleep," he demanded. "It's late." Agnès cleared away the mess she had made and curled up on her bed. Tomorrow she would start on a carving of the Birdman's flying machine. She would show the Falco flying through the sky with the other birds, up where it belonged.

17

When the prison guard returned, early the next morning, he unlocked Agnès's door and opened it wide.

"Follow me!" he demanded. Agnès got to her feet. As she stepped out into the passageway, the guard grabbed her by the arm and marched her off.

"Where are we going?" she said, trying not to trip and stumble. The guard said nothing as he led her along the dark passageway. Pale faces peered out like ghosts. A mean-looking hound, chained to the wall, snapped and snarled as they passed by. When they came to a heavy iron door, the guard knocked and waited.

"Come!" a voice called out. Agnès was led into a room with chains, fetters and grisly weapons arrayed on every wall. A black hat and cape hung by the door. Across the room, Lupus sat writing in a ledger that lay open on his desk.

"I've been expecting you," said the Marshal, looking up. Agnès didn't say a word.

"I went to visit Mother Superior at the convent yesterday," said Lupus, "to take her the statue." Agnès shook her head.

"But I didn't steal it," she said.

"So I understand," said Lupus. "Mother Superior told me

that she gave it to you." Agnès took a step forwards.

"Then I can go free?" she said.

"Not so fast," said the Marshal. "There is still the matter of the assault." Agnès stared in disbelief.

"The assault?"

"Yes, your attack on a Marshal of the law."

"It was an accident," Agnès protested, welling up at the injustice of it all. Lupus looked her in the eyes. He seemed to relish in her every sob and squirm.

"Do you know how much it costs to release a prisoner?" he said. Agnès shook her head.

"A hundred ecus," said Lupus.

"But I don't have that sort of money," said Agnès.

"Then you should be grateful for one who does," said the Marshal. He dipped his quill in a pot of ink and wrote in his ledger.

"Grateful to who?" said Agnès. Lupus signalled to the guard.

"Set the girl free—she's at liberty to go," he called out. Agnès took another step.

"But who?"

"You are free to go, so be gone!" insisted the Marshal. The guard grabbed Agnès by the arm and led her away. He marched her back along the passageway, past the snarling dog and the ghostly faces. When they reached the tower gate, the guard opened up.

Agnès stepped out onto the castle rampart. She felt bewildered and confused. Walking slowly, she descended to the busy marketplace below where doves pecked and fluttered, and the townsfolk of Amboise went back and forth. A young sister, wearing the familiar gown and wimple of the Minimes Convent, was standing by the water fountain. She walked over and greeted Agnès warmly.

"I'm Sister Excelsior," she said.

"I know," said Agnès. "You opened the door to me the other day."

"I was sent to find you," said Sister Excelsior. "The Reverend Mother wishes to speak with you urgently."

"If it's about the statue, I can explain," said Agnès. Sister Excelsior shook her head.

"No, it's not about the statue," she said. Setting off briskly, she led the way along the banks of the Loire, back to the Minimes Convent.

When they reached the Reverend Mother's door, Sister Excelsior knocked and waited. After a few moments, Mother Superior stepped out and gestured for Agnès to come inside. Agnès sat on a low wooden stool. She felt nervous and sheepish for having run away without saying a single word. The Reverend Mother sat down.

"Agnès, there's something I need to tell you," she said. "It's about your father."

"My father!" said Agnès. "Has he returned?" Mother

Superior looked her in the eye.

"What I need to tell you," she continued, "is that your father is never coming back." Agnès furrowed her brow.

"But of course he's coming back," she said. "He promised." Mother Superior bowed her head.

"I know," she said. "But I'm afraid he can't—you see, your father died before he could fulfil that promise." Agnès stared at the Reverend Mother in disbelief.

"That's not true," she said. "Who told you all this?"

"A man by the name of Fernando Suarez came to the convent about a month after you ran away," said Mother Superior. "He told me what happened." Agnès shook her head. Hot tears welled up in her eyes.

"He was lying," she said. "It can't be true."

"Signor Suarez was your father's friend," said Mother Superior. "They embarked on a journey together to the Americas." Tears coursed down Agnès's face.

"But how?" she said softly.

"Your father died of a fever," said Mother Superior. She reached out. Agnès pulled away. She felt numb. It was as if some terrible demon had opened wide its mouth and devoured her very soul. Everything she had ever hoped for had been snatched away in one cruel moment.

Mother Superior got up and went over to a large chest by the wall. She lifted the lid and took out a battered and worn leather bag.

"Signor Suarez left you this," she said. Agnès wiped away her tears. She stared at the bag.

"What's in it?" she asked.

"It belonged to your father," said the Reverend Mother. "He carried it with him to the Americas." Working open the buckle, she took out a small book. It was bound in red leather and had worn edges.

She gave the book to Agnès and explained that it was her father's journal. It was a record he had kept of his travels across the sea. Agnès stared down at the book. She couldn't bring herself to open it.

"This also belongs to you," said the Reverend Mother, reaching into the bag and taking out a certificate. She unfolded it and read it out.

Be it known to all persons, present and to come, that this document hereby confirms that Signor Fernando Suarez of Placencia Spain, has faithfully deposited the sum of eighty-thousand gold ecus in the keeping of the treasurer of Amboise exclusively for the benefit of Mademoiselle Agnès Desmarais.

In the presence of me, Notary Borean.

"Eighty-thousand ecus!" gasped Agnès. Mother Superior nodded.

"It was your father's share of a great fortune from the Americas," she said. Agnès suddenly had a thought.

"Did his money pay for my release?" she asked. The Reverend Mother gave a nod.

"Yes, when Marshal Lupus told me you were in prison, I asked the treasurer to pay for your release with some of the money," she said. Folding up the certificate, and tucking it back in the envelope, she handed it to Agnès.

"Now, take this to Monsieur Borean at the Treasurer's

House," she said. "He will pay you whatever you need, but do be wise."

"I've been a great bother to you haven't I?" said Agnès. Mother Superior shook her head.

"Not at all," she said. "You have only ever tried to follow your heart." Picking up the letter and her father's bag, Agnès got up to leave.

"I will come back and see you," she said. "This time I promise."

"I look forward to hearing how you get on," said the Reverend Mother. She drew Agnès close and placed a holy kiss on her forehead.

"Thank you," said Agnès. She turned and headed for the door, clutching her papa's bag tightly and wondering what she might possibly do with so much money.

18

Sitting on the banks of the Loire, beside the bridge of seven arches, Agnès watched a flock of wading birds as they pecked and poked in the shallows along the riverbank. She welled up every time she thought about her papa.

Unclasping the buckle of his travel bag, she reached inside and took out his journal. Wiping her eyes, she opened it up and turned the pages. The book was crammed full of his writing. However, like the Birdman's jottings, nothing of what her father had written made any sense at all. The journal was impossible to read.

"What language is this?" thought Agnès. "Why can't I read it?" Some of the pages had drawings on them. There were pictures of ships, sea creatures, ancient ruins and forest beasts. Laying aside the journal, she took out the treasurer's certificate and read it out loud. "Eighty-thousand gold ecus," she repeated over and over, trying to convince herself that it was for real.

As she sat there, the words of Bertrand's song echoed in her mind. When she thought about Pepin, still locked away in that dark tower, a wonderful thought came to her. Like a flame that burns brighter and brighter, it grew until it lit up her entire mind.

Agnès knew exactly what she must do. She leapt up and set off along the river bank. When she got to the corner, by the church of Saint-Florentin, she crossed over to the Treasurer's House on the other side. Hurrying up the steps, she entered the foyer of the white stone edifice. The place was very grand. Fine tapestries and paintings hung on the walls. A wiry clerk with a high collar came out. He looked rather surprised to see such a scruffy-looking girl in a ragged kirtle waiting in the foyer. Agnès held out her certificate.

"I'd like to see the treasurer," she said. The clerk checked over the document. He went through a doorway and returned a few moments later.

"Monsieur Borean will see you in his office," he said. Agnès followed the clerk inside. Like the rest of the building, the treasurer's room was very stately. The walls were panelled with dark wood. Elaborate plasterwork adorned the ceiling. Monsieur Borean sat behind a large desk, surrounded by cabinets that were piled high with ledgers.

"I want to withdraw some money," said Agnès. Monsieur Borean looked at her certificate.

"Yes, I am fully aware of this account," he said. "Signor Suarez deposited the money here several months ago."

"I'd like three hundred ecus," said Agnès. Monsieur Borean

leaned forwards and looked Agnès squarely in the eyes.

"There are scoundrels out there who would have your riches in a trice," he said.

"I know," said Agnès. "I can take care of myself well enough."

"I hope you can," said the Treasurer. He instructed the clerk to fetch Agnès's money. When the wiry clerk came back, he was carrying three bulging money pouches. He set them down on the desk and Monsieur Borean reached over to his set of scales. He weighed each one in turn before handing them over. Agnès promptly stowed the money pouches in her father's travel bag and fastened up the buckle.

"Thank you," she said.

Passing through the doorway into the foyer, Agnès was eager to get on with the next part of her plan. Clutching her bag tightly, she hurried down the steps and headed along the main thoroughfare. When she came to the Château, she took a deep breath and walked up the rampart to the gates. She waved to the guard on the other side.

"You!" said the guard, seeing Agnès standing there. "What do you want?"

"I'm here to see the Marshal," said Agnès.

"Well, you can't," said the guard. "Not without an appointment." Unclasping her bag, Agnès took out a shiny coin from one of her pouches. She held it out.

"Here's my appointment," she said. The guard glanced

around. Reaching through the bars, he took the coin and slipped it in his pocket. He then unlocked the gate, let Agnès inside, and escorted her down the narrow passage to the Marshal's room.

"Wait here," said the guard. He knocked and disappeared inside. Agnès could hear the sound of muffled voices. When the guard came out, he was shaking his head.

"The Marshal is busy," he said.

"I don't need long," said Agnès.

"You heard what I said," insisted the guard. He grabbed her by the arm and started to drag her away. Slipping from the guard's grasp, Agnès pushed open Lupus's door and went inside.

"You have to see me," she pleaded. "I'm here on business." Lupus wasn't alone. Seated on the opposite side of the desk was a large man in a blue tunic with rows of shiny buttons. He had a neatly trimmed beard and a long moustache.

"Business," said Lupus, raising a quizzical brow. "What sort of business?"

"I'd like you to release a prisoner," said Agnès. The Marshal leaned back in his chair and folded his arms.

"What right have you to demand such a thing?" he said. Agnès reached into her bag. She took out one of her money pouches and emptied all the coins onto the desk.

"There," she said. "A hundred ecus is the ransom for a thief isn't it?" Lupus looked down at the money.

"It all depends which thief you have in mind," he said.

"Pepin Moreau," said Agnès. The Marshal shook his head.

"The boy is nothing but a worthless urchin," he said. "If I let him go, he'll steal again."

"No, he won't," said Agnès. "I'll make sure of it."

"Why are you so interested in the boy?" asked the Marshal. "Who is he to you?"

"He's my friend," said Agnès. The Marshal leaned back in his chair and stared coldly.

"No!" he said. "In fact, I should put you away for good; that money must be stolen." Agnès shook her head.

"I didn't steal it," she said. "It's mine." Lupus signalled to the guard.

"Lock her away," he said. "I've heard quite enough of this deception." Agnès took out the rest of her money.

"Please!" she said, holding out both bags of coins. "I can pay you three times the ransom." A hand reached out to stop her. It was the big man in the blue tunic—the one with shiny buttons. He had been sitting, twiddling his moustache, listening quietly to the whole thing.

"Hold on, Lupus!" said the man. He counted the coins on the Marshal's desk. "The girl says this money is hers—let her prove it." Agnès reached into her bag. She took out her certificate and held it out. The man read it slowly and gave a nod.

"She's right," he said, showing Lupus the certificate bearing the seal of the Royal Treasury. "The money is hers." The Marshal grew agitated.

"This is some sort of swindle," he said. "Thieves like her are full of tricks." The big man laughed out loud.

"Lupus, you old dog," he said. "Admit when you're beaten. This certificate is genuine—let the boy go." Lupus scowled. He reached for his quill, dipped it in a pot of black ink, and reluctantly recorded the transaction in his book.

"Set the boy free," he muttered, signalling to the guard. Agnès took back her certificate and stowed it in her bag with the rest of her money. She turned and followed the guard out of the Marshal's room, back along the narrow passageway, and out through the castle gates.

19

Standing by the water fountain with her gaze fixed on the tower gates, Agnès watched and waited for Pepin to come out. Her heart leapt when the guard finally set him free. She hurried up the rampart to greet him. When Pepin saw Agnès coming, his face lit up.

"Agnès, what are you doing here?" he said.

"Lupus let me go, so I came back for you," said Agnès.

"How did you get out?" Pepin asked. Agnès shook her head.

"It's a long story," she said. "All that matters is we're both free." She took out a pouch of coins and gave it to Pepin. "Take this to your mother at the poorhouse," she said. Pepin untied the drawstring and looked inside.

"Agnès, where did you get all this?" he said. "You didn't…"

"No, I didn't steal it," said Agnès. "The money is from my father."

"Has he come back?" said Pepin.

"He isn't coming back," said Agnès, shaking her head.

"What happened to him?" said Pepin. Agnès explained

everything.

"But you mustn't worry about me," she said.

"What will you do now?" asked Pepin.

"I'll figure something out," said Agnès.

"I have an idea," said Pepin. "You can stay with me and Mama and the twins." Agnès shook her head.

"I'll manage well enough on my own," she said. "I can take care of myself."

Sending Pepin on his way to the poorhouse, Agnès walked back along the river. She passed by the bridge and the convent. When she reached the rocky slope that led up to her clifftop hideaway, she hitched her bag onto her shoulder and started to climb.

At the top, she brushed aside a veil of cobwebs that hung over the cavern entrance. She stooped down and went inside. The place was just as she had left it. Her bed of straw looked soft and inviting compared to what she had been sleeping on. She went over to the old sea chest and lifted the lid. The Queen's dress was still bundled up inside. She pulled it out. The hem was muddy and torn. It was hardly fit for a pauper to wear, let alone a queen. Wrapped up in the dress were the Queen's slippers. Agnès carried them over to the cavern entrance. She tapped them together and scraped off all the dry mud.

Gazing along the river, she looked at all the houses and cottages. They looked so tiny. With her father's fortune, she could pay for a room in a fine house—even a mansion like Le

Cloux. Right now, though, she was just glad to be back in her own familiar place.

When she grew hungry, Agnès climbed back down the hillside and wandered along to the marketplace. Choosing what to eat took longer than expected. She had enough money to buy whatever she fancied, but making up her mind was hard. It felt like being back at the royal banquet. The stallholder watched her every move as she hovered over his table. In the end, she chose a few Turkish hats and other sweet cheeses, as well as an almond tart that she planned to share with Magellan if he showed up. The stallholder looked relieved when she took out her money and paid.

The same thing happened when Agnès went to buy new clothes at Tortigoise dress shop. One well-to-do lady turned up her nose when Agnès walked in. Another kept her distance when she saw her looking around. Madame Tortigoise helped Agnès choose something her size.

"This one suits you," said the shopkeeper.

Discarding her itchy kirtle, Agnès tried on the new dress. It was made of plain green linen with crisscrossed laces up the front.

"I'll take it," said Agnès, reaching into her bag for her money.

Wearing the dress, Agnès went to buy needles and thread and a pair of dressmaker's shears from the haberdasher. She aroused none of the same suspicions when she walked into the shop. In fact, the young assistant couldn't have been more welcoming, treating her like any other customer.

The next day, after finishing off her almond tart for breakfast, Agnès bundled up the Queen's dress and slippers and stuffed them in her bag. Finding a secluded spot on the banks of the Amasse, she sat and ate her last few Turkish hats. When she was full, she unrolled the Queen's dress. It was muddy and smelly. She plunged it into the flowing waters. Swirling it around, she washed away all the dirt and grime, then laid it out on the riverbank to dry. Making a start on the slippers, she rubbed them with wet sand to get off the most stubborn marks, then rinsed them with clean water.

Later on, back in her cavern, Agnès examined the torn dress and pulled out all the loose threads. Remembering what Sister Eunice had taught her back at the convent, she quickly set to work. She cut the dress above the tear and stitched the hem. As she sewed the Queen's dress, she sang the songs Pepin had taught her. She sang of goblins, faeries, mermaids and ogres. The time passed quickly and soon her work was done.

When darkness fell, Agnès lit a candle and took out a sheet of paper. Resting on the lid of the sea chest, she began to write a letter of apology to the Birdman, seeking his pardon for the shame she had brought on his household. She hoped he would still think kindly of her, despite her shameful ways.

When Agnès had finished the letter, she tucked it inside her bag. Taking out her papa's journal, she opened it up and leafed through its pages. She puzzled over the strange words her father had written, wondering if he had learnt some new language in that far-off land of the Americas, or had devised an alphabet of his own to keep his thoughts from prying eyes. She looked over his drawings of sailing ships, ocean creatures and great leviathans of the deep.

Closing up the journal, Agnès blew out her candle and nestled down on her mattress of straw. As she lay there in the dark, she heard an owl hoot. Her thoughts drifted and she began to see pictures in her mind. As though time itself had started to unravel, she saw herself wrapped in a blanket, huddled in her papa's little rowing boat, all those years ago. It was nighttime and the stars were out. A ghostly white spectre swooped low over the river and flew off into the night sky, hooting. She could hear the splash of the oars and the lapping of water against the side of the boat.

As the vision played out in her mind, Agnès saw her father pushing the boat from the riverbank in the grey light of dawn. Beyond the misty shore, she could see a cluster of small houses with smoke rising from their chimneys. Beyond them, she could see a tall spire. The place felt strangely familiar. It felt like home. Agnès could now see a small cottage. She heard someone singing. When she looked, she saw her mama sitting on the doorstep, peeling apples and humming softly. Her nut-brown hair hung down. A bright rainbow of colours shone all around her in brilliant hues. Agnès felt calm and peaceful inside. She felt that her mama was not so very far away.

20

With the Queen's dress washed and mended, and the letter to the Birdman tucked safely in her bag, Agnès set off early the next morning for the Manor of Le Cloux.

As she walked, she went over in her mind what she might say about running off on the night of the banquet. When she rounded the corner near the manor house wall, she spotted someone sitting by the side of the road. It was Pepin.

Pepin jumped up when he saw Agnès coming. He was all excited and couldn't wait to tell her about going back to the poorhouse—how his mama had wept for joy—and how they had moved back into their old cottage by the Amasse. Agnès smiled broadly.

"I'm so happy for you," she said. "Now you must do all you can to help her, and you must promise you'll never get in trouble with the Marshal again." Pepin gave a nod. He saw the bundle Agnès was carrying.

"What's that?" he asked.

"The dress I tore," said Agnès. "I mended it. And I've

written a letter of apology to the Birdman."

"What if he won't see you?" said Pepin.

"I wouldn't blame him," said Agnès. "He'd have every right not to." She invited Pepin along with a promise that he might get to see the flying machine. Pepin didn't take much persuading. He was all for it.

Agnès felt nervous as they approached the manor house gates. When Hugo saw her coming, he came down from his tower.

"You!" said the watchman with a huff. "I'm surprised to see you again, but I know who will be glad you're back."

"I'm here to apologise," said Agnès.

"And the boy?"

"His name is Pepin," said Agnès. "He's my friend."

After letting the two inside, Hugo went off to find Maturina. Moments later, the housekeeper came rushing out.

"Agnès, where have you been?" she cried, throwing her arms around her. "I was so worried about you." Agnès felt safe and secure in the housekeeper's warm embrace.

"It's a long story," she said.

"Then you had better come inside and tell me all about it," said Maturina. Leading the way into the kitchen, she put out a plate of bread and cheese and a bowl of sweetmeats on the table. Pepin looked at the tasty morsels with wide eyes.

As they sat and ate, Agnès told Maturina all about being locked up in the tower, where she had made friends with Pepin.

She explained about being set free, about her father's fate in the Americas, and the fortune he had left behind. When she had finished, Maturina reached across the table and clasped her by the hands.

"The tower is no place for either of you," she said. "But that's all in the past and you have been granted a new start." Agnès handed Maturina the dress and slippers.

"These belong to Queen Claude," she said.

"I'll have Anne take them back to the Château," said Maturina. "Her Majesty will hardly have noticed them missing." Agnès reached into her pocket and took out the red ruby pin.

"What shall I do with this?" she said.

"It belongs to Monsieur Balthasar," said Maturina. "He lives at the Manor of Touraine." Pepin looked as though he was about to say something, but his mouth was too full to get the words out. Agnès put the pin away and took out the letter she had written.

"This is for the Master," she said. "I hope he isn't still angry with me."

"Ah, you don't know about the Master do you?" she said.

"What do you mean?" said Agnès. "Is something the matter?" Maturina got up and went over to the fire. She reached for a ladle and stirred a pot of stew that was bubbling away. Tapping her ladle against the side of the pot, she began to explain what had happened.

"On the morning after the banquet, he was taking down his mechanical swan," she said. "He was up a ladder when he fell off in a swoon."

"Is he all right?" said Agnès.

"Monsieur Leveque, the physician, insists on plenty of bed rest," said Maturina. "The doctor says he mustn't get too excited or it might happen again."

"Can I see him?" said Agnès.

"You know, that might not be a bad idea," said Maturina. "The Master keeps asking what became of you." Putting down her ladle, she walked over to the door and beckoned for Agnès and Pepin to follow.

Together they climbed the stairs to the Master's chamber. Maturina knocked and led the way inside. When she folded back the shutters, daylight came flooding into the room, revealing a large four-poster bed that was ornately carved with lions, birds and twisted leaves. The Birdman was buried beneath a mound of covers.

"Look who has come to see you," said Maturina. The old man stirred.

"Not that infernal medic again I hope."

"Monsieur Leveque is not back until tomorrow," said Maturina. "It's Agnès, and she's brought along a friend."

"Agnès, where?" said the Birdman, popping up his head.

"I hope you are feeling better," said Agnès, stepping closer.

"Much better," said the Master. "And if it wasn't for that

131

Leveque fellow, I would have been up from my sickbed days ago."

"Your swan was amazing," said Agnès. "Especially when all the tiny paper birds flew out." The Birdman's eyes lit up.

"I'm glad you liked it," he said. "It was very popular—no small thanks to you." Agnès took out her letter of apology. The Birdman opened it up and read what she had put. When he had finished, Agnès said that the nobleman had been right to call her a thief.

"At least you have the courage to admit it," said the Birdman. "Which is more than can be said for Giacomo."

"Who's he?" said Pepin. The Birdman frowned.

"A devil of a boy," he said. "Giacomo Salai was nothing but a bother to me." Maturina leaned over and plumped up the pillows.

"Giacomo went back to Tuscany," she said.

"And good riddance when he did," said the Birdman. Agnès explained about her time in the tower, where she had resolved to change her ways.

"Never look back," said the Birdman. "Now you must walk the earth with your eyes turned skyward."

"Like you with your flying machine," said Agnès. The Birdman leaned back on his mound of pillows.

"The doctor forbids me from working on the Falco," he muttered.

"But what about your promise to the King?" said Agnès.

"It will have to wait," said the Birdman with a heavy sigh. "The flying machine is far from ready."

"What about Melzi—can't he finish it?" said Agnès.

"Melzi has never shown a jot of interest in the Falco," said the Birdman. "Not since the Swan Mountain disaster."

"If my papa was here, he would help you finish it," said Pepin. "He was a carpenter."

"Pepin's father died in the Swiss wars," said Agnès.

"Which battle was he in?" asked the Birdman.

"The battle of Marigolds, I think," said Pepin. The Birdman thought for a moment.

"You must mean the Battle of Marignano," he said. "I was there myself. King François and I met with the Pope to agree a treaty with the Swiss after the war was over."

"Mama said my father was a hero," said Pepin.

"Then you should be very proud of him," said the Master. He turned to Maturina.

"Where's my journal?" he said. "The one about my meeting with Pope Leo." Maturina went off and came back with a small book. The Birdman thumbed through the pages until he found what he was looking for.

"Here it is," he said. He read about his visit with Pope Leo the Tenth at the Vatican, and about seeing the Sistine Chapel and the works of Michelangelo. When he had finished, Maturina laid a hand on the Master's forehead.

"It's time you rested," she said. She straightened the

bedsheets and went to close up the shutters. Agnès placed the Birdman's diary on the table by his side and got up to leave.

"We'll come back and see you again," she said. The Birdman smiled.

"Make sure you do," he said. "I shall be waiting right here."

21

When Agnès caught up with Pepin and Maturina, they were standing on the balcony, looking out over the garden. A flock of starlings was pecking for worms on the lawn, and a prowling cat was getting ready to pounce. Maturina let out a sigh.

"The Master is not the man he used to be," she said. "His strength has all but gone out of him."

"Do you think it will come back?" said Agnès.

"I hope so," said Maturina. "It did last time."

"It happened to him before?" said Pepin. Maturina gave a nod.

"He once had a dreadful swoon and lost the use of his hand," she said. "He couldn't do a thing for weeks."

"What about your potions and stews," said Agnès. "Won't they help?" Maturina threw up her arms.

"My stew—I left it on the boil," she cried out, dashing off in a mad panic.

Agnès and Pepin leaned out over the balcony and watched the starlings on the lawn. When the stalking cat made its move, all the birds took to the air and flew to the safety of the treetops.

"They make it look so easy," said Agnès. "If the Falco could fly like that, the Birdman would soon be leaping from his sickbed."

Descending the stairway to the garden below, Agnès and Pepin set off across the lawn. They followed the path that led down to the stream and headed for the old barn. Pushing open the doors of the Birdman's workshop, Agnès led the way inside. When Pepin saw the flying machine hanging up, he went right over to it. Gazing at the wickerwork of sticks and struts, he pulled on the rope that hung from the tail. The Falco swayed back and forth, creaking and groaning as though some dormant spirit had been aroused within it.

"Did you hear that?" said Agnès.

"Hear what?" said Pepin.

"The Falco," said Agnès. "It spoke." Pepin frowned.

"What do you mean?" he said.

"I swear it said that it wants to fly," said Agnès. She knew it sounded ridiculous, but it was true—that's what she heard. Pepin didn't laugh and Agnès wondered if perhaps he had heard it too.

On their way back to the manor house, neither of them said a word. Crossing over the courtyard, Agnès was taken by surprise when she saw Anne coming the other way with her arms full of boxes. Both of them stopped dead in their tracks and stared at one another. Anne said she had come to deliver a few things for the Master. She said that the King had been sending her each day to see how he was getting on.

"You must think badly of me," said Agnès. Anne shook her head.

"I shouldn't have been so nosy," she said. "I could see you felt awkward about wearing the ruby pin."

"Well, now you know the truth about it," said Agnès. "I just need to give it back to the nobleman."

"You know who he is, don't you?" said Anne. Agnès nodded.

"Maturina told me his name is Monsieur Balthasar."

"That's right—he lives at the Manor of Touraine," said Anne.

"I know where that is," said Pepin. "It has stone lions outside the gates and an eagle on the roof."

"You look different," said Anne. "What have you done to your hair?" Agnès shrugged.

"A lot has happened since I ran away," she said. "Maybe I'll tell you about it some time."

After Anne had set off back to the Château, Agnès and Pepin climbed the stairs to the Master's study. Melzi was sitting at a table by the window with the shutters wide, sketching in a book with a stylus.

"Agnès you're back," he said, looking up as the two of them walked in. "I didn't think I would see you again."

"Well here I am," said Agnès. Melzi put down his stylus and Agnès introduced Pepin to him.

137

"I suppose you know about the Master?" said Melzi.

"That's why we came to find you. We need your help."

"My help with what?"

"The Falco wants to fly," said Agnès. "And we need you to help us finish it."

"You must be moonstruck," said Melzi. "I have no interest in flying machines."

"That's not true," said Agnès, "You were at Swan Mountain—you almost flew." Melzi's face dropped.

"I don't want to talk about that," he said. "Don't you know what happened?"

"This is different," said Agnès. "The Falco is nothing like the Cigno." Melzi shook his head.

"I won't do it," he said. "I'm an artist, not a bird."

"Think what it would mean to him," pleaded Agnès. "It has always been the Master's dream to build a flying machine. If we help him do it, I know he'll get better." Melzi looked up. A thin smile slowly spread across his face.

"It would mean everything to him wouldn't it?" he said.

"So you will help?"

"I suppose."

"Great!" said Pepin. "That settles it."

Once Melzi had made up his mind, he was as good as his word. He went in search of everything that the Birdman had written and sketched on the subject of flight: books, papers, drawings and rough jottings. He piled them up on a table by the window.

"Don't expect this to be easy," he said. "The Master has been trying to figure it out for years."

"This might help," said Agnès, holding up a picture of a bat's wing. Melzi nodded.

"The wings are the most important part," he said. "They create the power to lift." Pepin picked up a drawing of a hawk. Melzi read out what the Birdman had written beneath it:

A bird is an instrument working according to mathematical law.

"How can you read that?" said Agnès, staring at the Birdman's odd writing. Melzi reached for a mirror and held it up beside the writing.

"Try now," he said. Agnès looked in the mirror.

"He writes backwards!" she said excitedly. "So that's why I couldn't read it."

"The Master is left-handed," Melzi explained. "Writing from right to left stops him smudging the ink." Searching through the Master's pile of papers, he found one entitled:

Studies of a Bird's Wing

Melzi didn't need a mirror to decipher the Master's words. He was perfectly used to reading them backwards. He read:

The muscles of a bird's wing are far more powerful than those of a man's arm.

"That's what he said about the Pipistrello," said Agnès. "Humans haven't got the strength to fly like a bird." Pepin found a drawing of a wing with pulleys and ropes attached to it. It was one of the Birdman's early plans for the Falco.

"Look here," he said. "I think this is the answer." Melzi examined the drawing and nodded.

"Indeed," he said. "It is a known fact that pulleys can double the strength of a man's arm." Agnès was sure that the Falco would fly if they followed the Birdman's plans exactly. Pepin was eager to make a start.

"What are we waiting for?" he said.

"Not so fast," said Melzi. "We can't do this on our own." He rightly pointed out that there was timber to be shaped, iron fastenings to be forged, and yards of silk to stitch. It would take specialist knowledge and expert skills to build a flying machine.

As they tidied up all the papers on the table and put away the Master's books, they each came up with a plan. Melzi said he would ask the carpenters at the Château to lend a hand. Agnès said she would ask the sisters at the convent to help with sewing the wings. Pepin suddenly remembered that he had promised his mama he wouldn't be late home. Agnès agreed to walk with him to the cottage. She told Melzi they would be back first thing in the morning to make a start with their plans.

22

Maturina was walking back from the henhouse with a basket of eggs when Agnès and Pepin spotted her on their way out. They told her everything about their plan to finish the flying machine and how Melzi had agreed to help.

Maturina said she was worried about what the Master might think. If he knew they were tampering with the Falco, he would have something to say about it, she told them.

"It's his pride and joy," she said. "What if you do more harm than good?"

"But you said it yourself—all the strength has gone out of him," said Agnès. "He can't finish it on his own, and Melzi will make sure it's done properly." In the end, Maturina promised not to breathe a word of it to the Master. It would be a surprise that would lift his spirits.

As they walked back to Amboise, Agnès thought about how she might persuade Mother Superior to let the sisters help. They spent many hours mending clothes for the poor. Surely the prospect of sewing wings for a flying machine would come as a welcome break.

"I know who else can help," said Pepin. "Someone who knows all about wood."

"Go on," said Agnès.

"Bertrand," said Pepin. "He's a master craftsman."

"And you know where to find him?" said Agnès.

"Of course," said Pepin. "Follow me." Racing off, he headed straight for the tavern. Agnès hurried after him. When they got there, Pepin went over to an old woman who was sitting on a step by the tavern door, weaving a basket.

"Where's Bertrand?" he asked.

"Try the parlour," said the old woman, pointing. As they passed through the noisy tavern, Agnès noticed all sorts of curiosities, arranged on window ledges and shelves. They were souvenirs from distant lands, left behind by travellers. Each had a label on it. There was a tea kettle from Japan, a skull drum from Tibet, brass figurines from India and strange masks from darkest Africa. One gruesome curiosity was a tiny human head. Its mouth had been sewn shut, and its hair was decorated with coloured beads.

As Agnès and Pepin stepped into the parlour, Monsieur Pascal, the innkeeper, swept past with a flagon of ale in each hand. He carried them over to two men who were sitting, talking. One had fiery red hair and was complaining about his meagre rate of pay.

"Barely four sous a day is all I get," he was saying, slopping ale on the table as Monsieur Pascal handed him his flagon.

"They only pay me five sous and I'm a skilled craftsman," said the other man. He was clean-shaven and had short dark hair. He spoke with a thick accent, like someone from the North. "I can hardly afford my bedchamber or this ale," the man went on. Pepin gave Agnès a nudge.

"That's him," he said, pointing to the short-haired fellow. Agnès went over.

"We can help," she said. The two men looked up.

"Excuse me," said the fiery-haired one. "You can help us?"

"I'll pay you twice what you earn now," said Agnès. The men looked at one another and frowned.

"Doing what?" said the short-haired fellow.

"Building a flying machine," said Agnès. The men both laughed.

"I know what you're thinking," said Agnès. "But the machine is already half finished, and we have proper plans." The short-haired fellow looked around at Pepin.

"Don't I know you?" he said. Pepin smiled and nodded.

"I was with you in the tower," he said. The man's eyes lit up.

"Pepin," he said, resting a hand on the boy's shoulder. "Lupus set you free. I told you never to give up hope."

"You're Bertrand aren't you?" said Agnès. "Pepin told me all about you." The man gave a nod.

"And this is my good friend, Roland," he said. "He's the finest bow-maker in all of Amboise."

"We need your help," said Agnès. "You're both skilled

craftsmen aren't you?" She reached into her pocket and took out two silver coins.

"Take these," she said. "I'll pay you the rest when the flying machine is finished." The men stared at the money.

"When do we start?" said Roland.

"Tomorrow morning at eight," said Agnès, "at the Manor of Le Cloux."

23

As she walked off, Agnès couldn't help wondering if the two men would show up the next day.

"They must think we're crazy?" she said. Pepin didn't look so worried.

"You don't need to fret about Bertrand," he said. "He'll come—you'll see."

When they got to Pepin's cottage down by the Amasse, Agnès recognised the place at once. The walls were painted white and the shutters were blue, just as he had said. Yellow and pink roses twisted and twined in an arch over the doorway. Pepin's mama was standing by the door, feeding crumbs to the birds. She had on a blue dress. Her hair was long and dark, and her complexion was olive. Two small girls stood clutching the folds of her apron.

"You must be Ida and Eva," said Agnès, walking up. The girls hid their faces.

"And you must be Agnès," said Pepin's mama, reaching out and greeting her warmly. She led the way into the parlour. The little downstairs room was as welcoming as Madame Moreau herself. She reminded Agnès very much of Mother Superior. She had that same expression of gentle composure in her eyes.

"I'm so glad you got your cottage back," said Agnès. Pepin's mama smiled.

"Thank you," she said, "I don't know how to ever repay you." Agnès shook her head.

"There's no need," she said. Noticing a collection of pictures and ornaments arranged on the mantel, she went over and picked one up. It was a small oval painting of a man in military uniform.

"Is this your husband?" she asked.

"Yes," said Madame Moreau. "His name was Etienne Moreau."

"Pepin told me he was very brave," said Agnès.

"He saved a mother and her children from a burning house," said Madame Moreau.

"You must be very proud of him," said Agnès. Pepin's mama nodded and smiled.

"I think of him all the time," she said. "Sometimes, I imagine he's sitting in that chair over by the window. As I sew, I tell him all my cares." Agnès put the oval painting back on the mantel. She thought how awful it must have been for the poor woman, losing her husband like that.

"Pepin told me you're good at sewing," she said. Madame Moreau nodded.

"I used to work as a seamstress," she said. "You must let me make some dresses for you—It's the least I can do." She went to the kitchen and came back with a basket of bread. Pepin helped himself to a crust.

"Go on Mama, ask her," he said. Madame Moreau turned to Agnès.

"We have a spare room," she said. "Why don't you stay with us?" Agnès thought for a moment.

"Thank you," she said. "Just until I get sorted out if that's all right."

"Of course," said Madame Moreau. "I'll make up the bed right away."

After finishing off a whole bread cake, Agnès said she had a few things back at the cavern that she wanted to get, and that she needed to visit someone.

As the birds flew home to roost, she made her way along the banks of the Amasse to the Loire. Stopping by at the convent to see Mother Superior, she told her all about the Birdman's incredible flying machine. She explained how he had spent many years trying to build it but was now too weak to complete his work. She explained about needing help to sew the wings. Mother Superior listened with great interest. She gazed up at a painting of angels on the wall.

"Will four sisters be enough?" she asked. Agnès nodded. In return for the help, she promised to donate a good sum of money to the Poor House of Saint-Lazarus.

After her visit to the convent, Agnès made her way back up the hillside to her cavern. She went over in her mind all that had happened that day and considered what she was about to do. She collected a few possessions: her bird drawings, her mirror and a few treasured trinkets, before making her way back to Madame Moreau's cottage.

Climbing the narrow stairs to her attic room, Agnès pushed open the door and went inside. The place was small but homely. The bed looked heavenly. Over by the window was a table and a small chair. She hung her father's bag on the chair back and opened the window wide. Leaning out, she could see ducks, geese and moorhens huddled in the rushes below. Bats were flitting and fluttering about over the water.

When the light faded completely, Agnès lit an oil lamp. Unclasping the buckle of her father's travel bag, she took out its treasures one by one and arranged them neatly on the table. As well as the rest of her money from the treasurer, there were a few Spanish cobs. She found a pendant with a lock of hair inside that she thought must be her mama's. There was the leather-bound journal her papa had kept, along with a quill and an inkpot with a tight stopper in it. Agnès opened up the journal. She stared down at the first page. Nothing her father had written made any sense at all.

Remembering the Birdman's strange mirror writing, she suddenly had a curious thought. She reached for her broken shard of mirror glass and held it up to the edge of the page. As if a spell had been broken, her papa's words suddenly appeared. Excitedly, she read them out loud.

Jacques Desmarais, His Book.

An account of his marvellous adventures in the
NEW WORLD.
Written for Agnès, that one day she might
know how her father went in search of his
fortune and discovered the treasures of El Rey
Dorado.

Anno Domini Fifteen Hundred and Fourteen.

Holding the mirror steady, and slowly tracing her finger
along the lines from right to left, Agnès read the first of many
entries.

June Eighth 1514

*A week has now passed since my journey
began. The Fates have called me up, and I feel
compelled to follow after them. Life at Muides
is no longer bearable after the death of my
beloved wife, Céline.*

*After paying my last respects at the
graveside of my 'Nightingale of the Marshes', I
travelled by boat with little Agnès to Amboise.
After entrusting her into the safe keeping of
the Sisters of the Minimes Convent, I worked*

my passage aboard the Espadon to the port of Saint-Nazaire on the Atlantic Coast. There, I boarded a vessel bound for Spain.

Parting with Agnès has caused me great sorrow. But it is all for the best. I trust that the Sisters will take good care of her until I return. My desire is that I can find my fortune across the sea and one day give her a rich and happy life.

Since hearing of the New World, I have known that it is my destiny to go there. It is said that a man may discover great riches in that distant land. There is talk of a city of gold in the mountains and a King they call El Rey Dorado.

Having purchased this journal and a quantity of ink at Saint-Nazaire, I feel compelled to record the particulars of my journey. Should anything happen to me along the way, and my quest come to nought, then I wish for Agnès to read these words and know that I did all that I could for her.

When she thought about her father's quest, Agnès felt warm tears well up in her eyes. She pictured him sailing off all those years ago with a bright hope burning inside—a hope that one day, life would be better for the two of them. She knew that he would never return but felt closer to him than ever before. In some small measure, the journal had brought her papa home again.

24

Early the next morning, Agnès waited with Pepin by the manor house gates. She had brought along two parcels, tied up with string. One was full of sweet comfits. The other was her collection of bird drawings. A thin mist hung in the air, and it was hard to see more than a few paces ahead. She kept glancing up at Hugo who was standing guard on the wall, sharpening his pike with a rough pumice stone. When she heard voices, Agnès saw two veiled figures emerge from the haze and fog.

"They're here," she called out. Pepin ran ahead to greet Bertrand and Roland, and Hugo came down from his watchtower to open up. He unbolted the gates and the two men walked in, carrying a heavy canvas bag between them.

"What do you have there?" Hugo asked, prodding at the bag with his pike.

"Tools," said Bertrand, opening up the flap so that the watchman could see inside. When Melzi appeared with a bundle of papers tucked under his arm, he frowned at the sight of the two men standing there.

"Who are they?" he asked.

"Experts," said Pepin. "That's what you wanted wasn't it?"

"What are your skills?" Melzi asked the men.

"I'm a woodcarver by trade," said Bertrand, "and my friend here is a skilled bow-maker."

"We've been told about the flying machine," said Roland.

"All right," said Melzi, "let me show it to you." Bertrand and Roland picked up their tools.

With Melzi leading the way, everyone headed down to the workshop. They crossed over the bridge and continued along the woodland path to the Birdman's little factory by the stream. Agnès opened up the doors, and they all went in and gathered beneath the outstretched wings of the Falco. Bertrand and Roland walked around the flying machine, inspecting it from every angle.

"This is very fine workmanship," said Bertrand, checking the construction carefully. "Who built it?"

"The Master of Le Cloux," said Agnès. "He built it all by himself, but now he's too ill to carry on."

"That's why we need your help," said Pepin. Melzi unrolled the papers he was carrying and spread them on the workbench.

"These are our plans," he said. The two men looked over the design carefully. Melzi had checked each detail of the Falco's construction and had written down the size of every strut, beam and length of fabric.

"And you expect it to fly?" said Roland, looking up at the Falco.

"Of course," said Pepin, enthusiastically.

"What makes you so sure?" said Bertrand.

"Mathematics," said Agnès. "It's all about getting the calculations right—the Master said so." Bertrand thought for a moment.

"We could trial it first," he said. He looked over at the Birdman's flying models hanging down: his bats and birds and dragonflies.

"You mean we could build a prototype?" said Melzi. Roland nodded.

"That way, it can be checked before we make any changes to the Falco," he said.

Melzi agreed it was a good idea. He gave the men a tour of the workshop and showed them all the wood and materials that they had to work with. Unpacking their tools, Bertrand and Roland rolled up their sleeves and quickly set to work on a miniature flying machine.

With the task of building a model Falco underway, Agnès and Pepin went over to the manor house to visit the Birdman. Maturina was busy baking curd tarts in the kitchen when they walked in. She had one lot on a cooling rack by the window and another on the fire. The table was covered with flour and pastry, and the smell of lemons filled the air.

"Can we see the Master today?" Agnès asked.

"I don't see why not," said Maturina. "He was a little brighter when he first woke up this morning."

Agnès set off up the stairs with her parcels whilst Pepin helped himself to a tart. He quickly followed after her, wiping crumbs from his hands and face as he went.

The Birdman was sitting beneath the covers, propped up on a mound of pillows. His face lit up when Agnès and Pepin walked in.

"You look much better today," said Agnès, pulling up a stool and sitting by the bedside.

"How is the weather today?" asked the Birdman.

"Misty," said Pepin, opening the shutters a little wider. The Birdman looked out.

"Be patient," he said. "Above the mist and the rain, the sun is waiting to shine through."

"I have a gift for you," said Agnès, holding out a small parcel. The old man worked apart the string with eager fingers.

"Anise comfits! My favourites," he said. "How did you know?"

"You ate a whole plate of them at the banquet," said Agnès.

"I could hardly let them go to waste," said the Birdman. He offered Agnès and Pepin one each, after picking out the largest piece for himself.

"You look much better," said Agnès.

155

"I feel as light as a feather," said the Birdman. "In fact, I had a very strange dream about it last night." After chewing and thinking for a moment, he related the whole thing.

"I dreamt that I was sitting in my favourite chair. Gulls were flying high over my head, soaring and circling in a great throng. To my astonishment, the whole lot swooped down on me. They lifted me up by the skirts of my nightshirt and the hair of my head. They carried me away, flapping their wings so furiously that I could hardly hear my own cries for help."

"It sounds like a nightmare," said Pepin.

"That wasn't the whole of it," said the Birdman, resting back on his mound of pillows.

"The gulls carried me over land and sea. They flew me across the waves, farther than the eye can see. At last, we arrived over a land of forests and rivers. I looked down and saw a golden palace, perched high in the mountaintops. When the birds flew me down, I was greeted by such a King as I have never seen before. He was covered from head to foot in gold."

"And then what happened?" said Agnès, perched on the edge of her stool.

"Then I woke up," said the Birdman.

"What do you think it means?" said Pepin.

"I have no idea?" said the Birdman, leaning forwards and picking out another anise comfit. "Sometimes there is no sense at all to such dreams." Agnès thought about the city in the mountains and the king of gold.

"Have you ever heard of El Rey Dorado?" she said at last.

"Can't say I have," said the Birdman.

"My father was an explorer in the Americas," explained Agnès. "He went looking for a city of gold in the mountains."

"And you think that's what I saw in my dream?" said the Birdman. Agnès shrugged.

"It does sound a lot like it," she said. The Birdman scratched his head.

"Maybe so," he said, "but how it all ended up in my dream, I can't quite imagine."

Agnès handed the Birdman the other parcel she had brought along and watched him unwrap it. It was her collection of bird drawings. The Birdman examined each one in turn, as Pepin leaned in for a closer look.

"Are these all your own work?" asked the Birdman. Agnès gave a nod.

"Ben fatto!" said the Master. "I am most impressed."

"I have never shown them to anyone before," said Agnès. The Birdman looked up.

"A gift like yours should not be kept hidden," he said. "This is a very fine tawny owl."

"It took me ages to do all the feathers," said Agnès. The Birdman said how much he admired the shading. He leaned back and closed his eyes.

"You have a rare talent," he said. "In all my years, I can't

157

remember seeing such artistic promise in one so young." Agnès sat a little taller.

"Some of my pictures need finishing," she said. The Master shook his head slowly.

"Art is never finished," he said. "Believe me—I know all about that."

25

After visiting the Birdman, Pepin went to see how Bertrand and Roland were getting on. Agnès, meanwhile, went to find a quiet spot in the garden where she could sit and read. She wandered down past the stream and perched on a log. Opening up her papa's journal, she turned to the day he embarked on his long voyage across the sea. Now that she was familiar with his backwards way of writing, she no longer needed a mirror to read it.

June Fourteenth 1514

After sailing five days due south from the port of Saint-Nazaire, we have, at last, reached the Spanish mainland and the Bay of Santander. The entrance to the bay is a very narrow neck of water. The harbour is full of vessels from every port in the world. There are fishers and whalers, merchants and mariners of every nationality and tongue. After many enquiries, I discovered that the Espiritu, a caravel of four masts, is due to sail on the morrow. The vessel is destined for the colony at Santa Maria in the Americas. We have joined with Signor Núñez de Balboa and an expedition of men who are all resolved to seek for gold and riches. They speak of the treasures of El Rey Dorado, the Golden King. Our captain says we shall sail at first light. Fair seas and light winds are expected from the east. All the men are in high spirits, talking of a great fortune to be had.

Agnès thought about her own journey of discovery and the adventure she was about to embark upon. Like her father, her spirits were high and she was excited to see what progress had been made. By the time she arrived at the barn, Bertrand and Roland had completed the miniature flying machine. It was small and light, and it had a skin of thin fabric stitched to its wings. Agnès marvelled at how closely Roland and Bertrand had followed every detail of the Birdman's plans.

"How did you manage to shape the wood and join it like that?" she asked.

"It's all about having the right tools," said Bertrand.

"And years of practise," said Roland.

Impressed with the results, Agnès and Pepin went to find Melzi. After inspecting the work for himself, Melzi pointed to a small window at the top of the manor house.

"We can launch it from up there," he said. Carrying the

miniature flying machine, a ball of string and a parsnip that Agnès fetched from the kitchen, they all set off up the narrow steps to the little garret room. At the top of the stairs, Melzi reached into his pocket for a key and unlocked the door. Hinges creaked as he pushed the door open. Brushing aside a veil of cobwebs, he led the way inside. The room was dry and dusty. A smell of old sackcloth hung in the air.

"No one has been up here since King Louis died," said Melzi. He went over to the window and worked open the latch. Agnès looked out.

"Perfect!" she said, gazing out across the lawn towards a tall plane tree in the distance. Bertrand and Roland were standing on the edge of the courtyard, looking up in eager anticipation.

Melzi looked over the miniature Falco. He checked that all the joints and struts were secure and that nothing had worked loose. Wrapping string around one of the parsnips, he tied it underneath.

"That should do it," he said, tugging on the parsnip. "Behold, the first flying vegetable."

"Throw it hard and straight," said Agnès. Melzi walked over to the window. He counted to three then launched the little craft through the opening with a firm shove. As the Falco left his hand, it tipped to one side. The flying machine twisted and twirled like a sycamore seed in the wind. Agnès caught a fleeting glimpse of it as it fell out of sight. On hearing a dull thud, everyone hurried down to the courtyard where they discovered the parsnip snarled up in a tangle of wood and crumpled silk. When Agnès picked it up, the end of the parsnip broke off.

"Not a good start," said Melzi, glumly. Bertrand and Roland came over to inspect the wreckage. They said the damage wasn't as bad as it looked and shouldn't take long to repair.

Agnès refused to be put off by the setback. She remembered something the Birdman had said about getting the balance just right.

Back at the workshop, Bertrand and Roland fixed up the little Falco. When they had finished, it was as good as new. Agnès tied on a fresh parsnip. This time, she suspended it a little lower and on a steeper angle.

"What are you doing?" said Pepin. Agnès looked up.

"I'm getting the balance right," she said. "Having the weight lower down will help." Melzi gave a nod.

"Good thinking," he said.

With the flying machine firmly in her grasp, Agnès led the way back up the steps to the room at the top of the manor house. As she leaned out of the window, the breeze ruffled her hair. Drawing back her arm, she took aim.

This time the miniature Falco flew off with its nose and tail perfectly level. It hung in the air with its wings steady, before dipping and diving over the courtyard and coming to rest on the edge of the lawn.

"That was a lot better," said Pepin.

"There's still something wrong," said Agnès, shaking her head. "We have to do better than that."

Flopping down on the dusty floorboards, everyone tried to figure out how to get the miniature Falco to fly longer and farther. Agnès pictured the birds soaring in never-ending spirals over the spires of the Château. She thought how effortlessly Magellan launched himself from rocky ledges and the tops of trees. With one mighty leap, he would rise up—just as he had done from the window ledge of her prison cell.

"That's the answer," she said. "One mighty leap." Pepin and Melzi looked at one another blankly.

"How will the Falco do that?" said Melzi. Agnès went over to the window and looked out. She thought about the day she visited the Château with Anne and saw archers practising with their bows.

"The same way an arrow does it," she said.

"You want to fire the Falco from a bow?" said Pepin.

"Exactly," said Agnès. "Hugo has crossbows doesn't he?" She set off back down the stairs and headed for the watchman's little guardhouse by the manor house gates. Pepin and Melzi followed after her, still not sure how this was all going to work. Crossing the courtyard, Melzi stopped to pick up the remains of the Falco. One of the wings was crumpled and the tail was twisted out of shape. He handed it to Bertrand and Roland, who quickly assessed the damage and set off back to the workshop to make the repairs.

Agnès hurried over to the guardhouse.

"Come on," she called back, pushing open the door and leading the way inside. A crossbow hung on the wall above the fireplace, just as she remembered. It was too high for her to reach, so she turned to Melzi.

"Don't just stand there," she said. "Help me get it down." Melzi stepped up to the fireplace, muttering under his breath. Lifting the bow down from the wall, he handed it to Agnès. All the while, Pepin kept a sharp lookout for Hugo.

With the crossbow slung over her shoulder, Agnès set off for the old barn, eager to see if Roland could make it launch a miniature flying machine.

Roland said he was familiar with the crossbow's firing mechanism. It had a groove cut out for the bolt to sit in. Halfway down the tiller was a slot for the sinews. Roland pulled back on a small firing lever that he called *the tickler*.

"All we have to do is add a narrow rod underneath the Falco so that it sits in the groove," he said. Melzi wasn't so sure.

"But the Falco isn't like a bolt—it has wings," he said. "Won't they get in the way?"

"Not if we angle them up a bit," said Roland. Bertrand gave a nod.

"That should do it," he said, "though we might need to strengthen them. This is a powerful crossbow and could do some damage."

As the two craftsmen worked to make all the changes, Agnès, Pepin and Melzi watched with intrigue. When the Falco was ready, Roland slid it back and forth in the groove of the crossbow to check it would launch correctly.

Back in the garret room, Agnès tied on a parsnip so that it dangled freely, without getting in the way. Melzi wound the handles of the crossbow, slowly drawing back the sinews until they clicked into place.

"That should do it," he said, offering the crossbow to Agnès. "It was your idea," he said. "You should be the one."

Agnès took hold of the crossbow. She carried it over to the window and looked down at Bertrand and Roland, waving up. In the distance, she could see the tall plane tree, its leaves rustling in the breeze. Melzi fitted the little flying machine into the groove of the crossbow.

"On the count of three, press down on the tickler," he said.

Agnès stood with her feet apart. She held the butt of the crossbow against her hip and pointed the Falco out through the open window. On the count of three, she pressed the trigger. The miniature Falco shot off at tremendous speed, rising up and arching through the sky.

"It's flying" cried Pepin, excitedly. Everyone watched with wide eyes as the Falco soared effortlessly over the courtyard. Bertrand and Roland stood cheering it on over the lawn. When it reached the other side, the nose of the flying machine dipped. Losing height fast, the Falco flew right into the low-hanging branches of the big plane tree.

"We did it," cried Pepin. "It flew." Melzi laid a hand on Agnès's shoulder.

"You were right," he said. "It just needed to take a giant leap."

"Now all we need is a much bigger crossbow," said Pepin.

Agnès smiled broadly.

"And I know where to get one," she said.

26

On a shelf in the Birdman's study, Agnès found the book of war machines. She lifted it down and turned to a drawing of a giant crossbow. The enormous catapult was so large that it had to be pulled by heavy horses.

"He designed it for the Duke of Milan?" said Melzi. Agnès nodded.

"If it can knock down castle walls, it must be powerful enough to launch the Falco," she said.

"But where do we get such a thing?" said Pepin.

"We build one," said Agnès. Melzi laughed.

"You're crazy," he said. "We can't do that."

"No, but I bet Roland can," said Pepin.

"And we can get the carpenters from the Château to help him," said Agnès. Melzi shook his head. Finishing the Falco would be hard enough, he said—building a giant crossbow on wheels was going a step too far. It was getting late, anyway, and he thought it was about time they called it a day.

As Agnès and Pepin walked back to the cottage in the cool of the evening, they talked excitedly about their plans. Melzi's doubts and qualms hadn't put them off one bit, and they were sure that the giant catapult was just what they needed to launch the flying machine.

Pepin's mama had supper ready when they arrived home, and the twins were already fast asleep in bed. After finishing off a bowl of broth and a large slice of bread, Agnès went up to her little attic room. She lit a lamp and took out her papa's journal and her mirror glass. Holding the mirror alongside the page, she began to read of his journey aboard the Espiritu.

June Twenty-First 1514

Our ship has been sailing due south along the African coast for almost six days now. We have seen nothing but fair seas and clear skies. I have sighted many dolphins that leap and dive. They are playful sprites and never tire of their sport. The captain has had me employed mending ropes and sails. We are taking root ginger for our seasickness, a condition that troubles even the hardiest of sailors.

June Twenty-Second 1514

We arrived this morning at the Great Island of Dogs and have taken on fresh water and provisions for our crossing of the Great Divide. We shall maintain a due westerly course. Many days sailing lie ahead of us. I have befriended a fellow seafarer by the name of Signor Fernando

Suarez. This is his third such voyage and he
says we should expect all manner of harsh
weather.

Agnès read of long days aboard the Espiritu, waiting for the winds to carry it across the vast ocean. She read of blistering days on deck, freezing nights in the hold, and weeks of toil and hardship. The voyage was terrible at times. Agnès wondered how the men had managed to survive. After seventy-seven days at sea, despite all odds against them, they finally reached that distant shore on the far side of the world.

August Thirteenth 1514

We sighted land at sundown and anchored
until the early hours of the morning. At first
light, we joined with Signor Núñez de Balboa
who came out to greet us with his faithful dog,
Leoncico. After rowing to shore with him and
his men, we were all overjoyed to be on dry
land once more. We camped by the walls of
a very ancient ruin and sampled a curious
black beverage, prepared for us by the natives.
Balboa told us of his quest for the South Sea
beyond the forests. He speaks of a city in
the mountains with gold and riches beyond
measure.

October Sixteenth 1514

Six weeks have passed since our arrival in this strange new world. We have travelled many miles and have encountered a land of forests and rivers. We must constantly beat our way through the thick jungle. Signor Balboa has told us more tales of El Rey Dorado. He says the king will freely give his gold in exchange for everyday items. My only regret is that Agnès is not here with me to see all of this. Perhaps, one day, she will embark on a journey of her own and will see what wonders there are in this world.

27

Agnès set off for the Manor of Le Cloux with her head full of plans and ideas. She waited at a bend in the road for Pepin—who was trailing behind, swinging a thin stick at clumps of long grass that sprouted by the wayside. White gulls soared in the pale morning sky. They seemed to range so effortlessly, with only the slightest of wing-beats. Agnès hoped that once the Falco was up there, it would do the same. She was convinced that the giant crossbow was still a good idea and hoped Melzi would come around to her way of thinking. When Pepin walked up, he was covered all over in grass seeds.

"What's the hurry?" he said.

"We have a big job ahead of us," said Agnès, "so get a move on!"

Hugo was surprised to see Agnès and Pepin up so early. Before anyone else arrived, they went down to the workshop and made a start by sweeping up all the sawdust and wood shavings. They tidied the workbenches and arranged pots of glue, spools of thread and bundles of cord. Pepin picked up some of the Master's tools. There were saws, planes, wood-shaves and chisels of all shapes and sizes. At the back of the barn was a small forge with an anvil and bellows. It was covered in dust and cobwebs and didn't look as if it had been lit for some time.

When Agnès and Pepin had finished their jobs, they walked back to the gatehouse. Sitting on the edge of the water trough, Agnès went over in her mind what might still be needed. She wanted to be sure that everyone had the right tools and materials to do a proper job. She dipped her hand in the water and tried to think of anything they might have forgotten.

When Bertrand and Roland came along, Hugo opened up the gates. Not long after, Agnès spotted the sisters from the convent. She went out to greet them and led them over to where the others were waiting.

"May I introduce Sisters Excelsior, Cathetel, Ecanas and Liwet from the Minimes Convent," she said. Bertrand offered his hand to each one, and Roland donned his cap.

As the workers from the Château walked up, Agnès counted seven in all, including two blacksmiths and a very big African that everyone called Goliath. One of the workers reported that the Captain of Arms was happy to let them build a giant catapult, on condition that it be handed over to the King's Arsenal afterwards.

"You told them about the crossbow," said Agnès, turning to Melzi. "So, you agree it's a good idea?"

"I thought it over," said Melzi. "I don't see why we can't build it."

The little band of workers crossed over the lawn and wandered down to the Birdman's workshop, chatting and admiring the bluebells and clumps of archangel along the way.

Once the Sisters had looked over the plans for the wings, they rolled out lengths of silky fabric, marked out where it needed cutting, then threaded their needles, ready to make a start.

Melzi explained to the carpenters about the giant crossbow. He laid out his plans, pointing to the launch skid and a large hook underneath the flying machine that would lock into the catapult's firing mechanism. The carpenters looked over the design and discussed how it might be done. Eventually, they began measuring and marking out enormous oak beams for its construction. Soon they were sawing and chopping the various sections into parts for the catapult.

Fearing they might get in the way, Agnès and Pepin went off to visit the Birdman. As they approached his bedchamber, Monsieur Leveque was just leaving. They waited for the doctor to go before knocking and going in. The Birdman was in a state of wild agitation, huffing and puffing testily.

"I have had far too much bed rest—it's driving me berserk," he ranted, tugging at his sheets. "That know-it-all physician treats me like an infant." Agnès handed him a bag of Turkish hats that she had brought along. The Birdman opened the bag but said he was in no mood for any right now.

"Maturina has been plying me with too much foreign cheese as it is," he said, patting his stomach. "It's causing me no end of discomfort, and I blame the cheese for all the strange dreams I've been having."

"You've had more dreams?" said Agnès. The Birdman shifted restlessly.

"Last night's vision was far stranger than the last," he said. Agnès pulled up a chair and Pepin leaned against the bedpost to listen. After patting his bloated stomach, the Birdman began.

"I was sitting beneath the old chestnut tree, reading a book. Before long, the leaves turned brown and fell to the ground. The next thing I knew, snow began to fall, and the garden was gripped by winter. I wrapped my cloak tight around me. No sooner had the earth frozen hard, than the snow and ice began to thaw. As the sun rose up, the chestnut tree burst forth with leaves of green and blossoms of white."

"Was that it?" said Pepin. The Birdman shook his head.

"It was only the start," he said, shifting restlessly.

"The entire episode repeated itself, only this time much more quickly. The leaves fell, the snows came, and winter turned to spring—all in the space of a few moments. And then, to my astonishment, it happened again. Over and over, I was spun about in a whirlpool of winters and summers until my mind was completely undone."

"And then what happened?" said Agnès, not sure where all

this was leading.

"When the passage of years ended, I gazed up and saw all manner of flying contraptions. Machines were flitting through the skies in marvellous ways. Some were spinning. Others were breathing out fire behind them. I saw men in giant bread-baskets, suspended beneath floating orbs of silk. Women were hanging on the breeze beneath rainbow-coloured parasols. I even saw Chinese firecrackers that shot to the moon and beyond, trailing fire and smoke behind them."

"And then?" said Agnès. The Birdman sighed.

"Then I came to my senses and realised that it was merely the dream of a foolish old man." Agnès sat back in her chair.

"You're hardly foolish," she said. "You're the most brilliant man I know."

"Hardly," said the Birdman. "I haven't yet built a flying machine that works, have I?" Agnès wondered if perhaps now was a good time to say something about what was going on. She looked around at Pepin.

"Shall we tell him?" she said. Pepin shrugged.

"What, you mean about building the flying machine?" he said. The Birdman sat up.

"What's this about the Falco?" he said. There was no going back. Agnès felt she had to say something.

"Look, we weren't going tell you," she said. "It was meant to be a secret."

"We're going to finish it for you," said Pepin, excitedly. A

175

look of great surprise spread across the Birdman's face.

"You're doing what?" he said.

"Melzi is helping us," said Agnès, hoping to smooth things out a bit. The Birdman's eyes grew wide with astonishment.

"Melzi is helping to build the flying machine?" he said, "But he never showed a jot of interest after what happened at Swan Mountain."

"He's interested now," said Pepin.

"Melzi has been a great help," said Agnès. She started to tell the Birdman all about it. "He made some changes to your design. We then flew a miniature Falco right across the lawn to the trees."

"You did what?" said the Birdman.

"We launched it from that little room at the top of the manor," said Agnès.

"But how did you get it to fly so far?" said the Birdman.

"It just needed a bit of help," said Pepin.

"We used a crossbow," said Agnès. The Birdman's face lit up.

"A crossbow," he said. "You fired it from a crossbow." Agnès nodded.

"Once it was up there, the wings took over and carried it all the way."

"By what means do you intend to launch the real Falco?" said the Birdman.

"We're going to build the giant crossbow you invented,"

said Agnès. "The one you designed for the Duke of Milan."
The Birdman slumped back on his mound of pillows.

"Why didn't I think of that?" he said, shaking his head.

"You did," said Agnès. "You invented the flying machine
and the crossbow." The Birdman stared out of the window,
wistfully.

"Yes, but you put them both together," he said. "You made
the connection." Agnès looked around at Pepin.

"I suppose we did, didn't we?" she said, proudly.

"But how do you intend to build the crossbow and finish
the Falco?" said the Birdman. "Such a task is daunting."

Agnès explained that they had lots of willing helpers.
She said that the Captain of Arms at the Château had sent
carpenters and blacksmiths, and Mother Superior had sent
sisters to help with the sewing."

"You have surrounded yourself with capable hands," said
the Birdman. "That is another thing I failed to do; I tried to
work alone."

"Yours was the hard part," said Agnès. "It was your dream
to build the flying machine and you already finished half of
it."

"Then we are very fortunate to have found one another,"
said the Birdman. "With my vision and your labours, the Falco
will at last rise up and fly."

28

A pleasant smell of pine tar and wood shavings greeted Agnès and Pepin as they walked into the busy workshop early the next morning. Bertrand and Roland had already worked up quite a lather, chopping and planing. They had bent and fixed all the struts that would give extra support to the Falco's wings. Measuring and checking, they crafted with great skill and care. They cut and tied ropes to the body and tail to strengthen it. Agnès watched as they pulled cords and knotted them in place, before trimming the frayed ends with a sharp blade and dipping them in hot wax.

Later on, Pepin's mama brought the twins, Ida and Eva, to see the Falco. She had been asking Pepin every day how things were progressing and wanted to see for herself what everyone was getting up to. The sisters had already sewn together strips of blue silk for the wings and had carefully snipped out white fleur-de-lis decorations. Pepin's mama was most impressed and offered to lend a hand while the twins went off to play.

"It makes such a change from mending old clothes," said

Sister Liwet.

"I hope it's not too noisy for you," said Madame Moreau.

"We like the noise," said Sister Ecanas. "Bertrand has been teaching us a song about a hat with three corners."

"And one about Lilofee and her lover from beneath the waves," said Sister Cathetel.

"And the seven sons of Adam," said Sister Liwet, "who snap their fingers and clap their hands and tap their feet."

Agnès wondered what Mother Superior might say about it all. But Pepin's mama said that, with everyone doing such a fine job, and in such high spirits, perhaps even she wouldn't mind.

As she looked along the path, Agnès spotted Maturina and Anne heading over, carrying a large pot between them.

"I hope everyone is hungry for some of my stewed dumplings," Maturina called out. The workers from the Château put down their tools, the sisters set aside their sewing, and everyone made their way over to a long trestle that had been set out with bowls and spoons on it. Even Pepin and the twins showed up when the waft of Maturina's stew drifted their way. Setting the pot down on the table, Maturina lifted the lid and gave it a stir.

Agnès looked over at Bertrand who was busy carving the head of an eagle.

"Aren't you hungry? she asked him.

"I'll let everyone else go first," said Bertrand.

"Your eagle head looks amazing," said Agnès. Bertrand said it was for the front of the flying machine, like the figurehead of a ship. He had hollowed it out to make it as light as possible.

Agnès went over for a closer look. She ran her hand over the beak. It was smooth to the touch. Each feather on the eagle's head had been etched with intricate lines.

"It's wonderful," she said.

"The vision of it was already in my mind," said Bertrand.

"Try yourself," he said, handing Agnès the mallet and chisel.

Clamping a piece of wood to the workbench, he sketched the shape of a feather on one side. Agnès tapped carefully with the mallet and carved along each charcoal line.

"Not bad," said Bertrand.

"It's not nearly as good as yours," said Agnès, handing back the tools.

"I've been carving for a long time," said Bertrand. "We all have to start somewhere."

"Let me try," said Pepin, putting down his bowl of stewed dumplings. Bertrand handed him the mallet and chisel and Pepin set to work, carving out a very fine feather of his own. It was as if he knew instinctively what to do. Pepin's mama looked on with pride.

"You are indeed the son of a woodcarver," she said. "It's in your blood."

When everyone had finished eating, Agnès and Anne went around collecting up all the empty bowls, and the workers went back to work. While the carpenters got on with shaping the wooden arms of the giant crossbow, the two blacksmiths fired-up the old forge at the back of the workshop. They mended the bellows and lit the coals. Soon, the forge was aglow.

Amidst the steam and heat, the men hammered and bent iron bars into sturdy brackets and fastenings for the giant catapult. With every strike on the anvil, Agnès covered her ears. She shielded her eyes as the men plunged seething red iron into a barrel of water, sending plumes of steam hissing all around.

Other workers sawed and chopped. They scraped, planed and hammered. The sisters and Madame Moreau carried on late into the afternoon, sewing the wings. Tap by tap and stitch by stitch, the work continued in the belly of the old barn. Agnès and Pepin helped out in any way they could. They fetched and carried, keeping the workers well supplied.

The little band of devoted helpers returned each day and continued all week long. Agnès came and went. She felt much happier about being seen around town and liked to spend time in the marketplace, buying gifts and treats that she took back for the workers.

One day, she spent the entire morning with Monsieur Etoffe, the weaver, picking out fabrics for Madame Moreau to stitch into clothes for her to wear. She chose a variety of colours in fine linen, taffeta and wool, to see her through the changing seasons. Each afternoon, she played games with Eva and Ida in Madame Moreau's parlour, while the talented seamstress cut and trimmed the cloth, gathering and stitching it into wonderful outfits.

Another time, Agnès went to visit the cobbler in his shop near the tavern. After measuring her feet, he cut and turned the uppers out of fine hide then glued and stitched them to soles of strong leather.

After Pepin's mama had finished making dresses for Agnès, she went back to the manor house to help the sisters. In fact, she couldn't stay away. She took along her sewing things and helped as much as she could. The Birdman kept sending down notes to the carpenters with his latest ideas and instructions. He spent every waking moment, sitting up in bed, revising his drawings and scribbling down his thoughts. He instructed Melzi to report back to him every step of the way.

Agnès checked on the progress of the flying machine regularly. One morning, she went especially early to see it. Through the barn doors, the Falco looked like a butterfly warming its wings in the sun. She went over and ran her hand over its sleek struts and finely stitched covering of blue silk. Bertrand's eagle-head now took pride of place at the front.

The giant crossbow was sturdy and strong. With solid wooden wheels, it could be pulled along by heavy horses. The Falco was nearly finished and the time had almost come for it to fly.

Agnès had enough money left over to pay everyone their wages and asked Anne to help her keep a record. They sat together at a table in the salon. Agnès counted, and Anne wrote it all down in a book. She paid the workers generously and gave a good amount to the poorhouse of Saint-Lazarus, just as she had promised Mother Superior she would.

After taking care of finances, Agnès went to help Maturina in the kitchen. She volunteered to peel vegetables for a hotpot to feed all the workers.

"You should be proud of yourself," said Maturina, untying a sack of carrots. "You have done a wonderful thing." Agnès reached for a knife.

"I haven't done much," she said, "Everyone else has done all the hard work."

"But you made it happen," said Maturina. "You were the one who believed in the Master's dream."

"The Falco hasn't flown yet," said Agnès, reaching for another carrot.

"But it will," said Maturina, "and the Master will be the happiest man alive when it does."

As she worked, Agnès could hear the sounds of hammering and singing in the distance. When the hammering stopped and voices turned to shouts, she looked out of the window to see what all the fuss was about. When Hugo dashed past, Agnès put down her knife and ran out. As she wandered across the courtyard, the watchman came dashing back the other way carrying empty buckets.

"What's going on?" Agnès called out.

"There's a fire," yelled Hugo, frantically. "The barn is on fire." Snatching up her skirts, Agnès ran after him. She raced over the lawn, her feet flying and her heart pounding as she went. Clattering over the wooden bridge, she crossed the stream, where Hugo had stopped to fill up his buckets.

When she got to the barn, the air was thick with smoke. Flames were lapping up through the roof timbers. Agnès stared in disbelief. Everyone was frantically scurrying back and forth with pails of water, doing their best to douse the flames. But it was no use. The raging fire was out of control, and the flames rose even higher.

Hit by a tremendous wall of heat, Agnès could hardly take another step. She watched in horror as blackened timbers twisted and crumbled. She shielded her face as roof shingles burst and splintered. And then, in one final act of terrible destruction, the barn roof collapsed, devouring everything beneath it. Burning timbers crashed down, engulfing the Falco in a fiery inferno.

Agnès turned away. She couldn't bear to look on a moment longer. When she heard a voice call out, she glanced around. It was Melzi.

"It's gone!" he cried. "The flying machine has gone."

29

As the flames died down, and the fire dwindled, others slowly emerged from the surrounding trees. Melzi made his way over to where Agnès was standing. His clothes and face were black with ash and soot.

"What happened?" said Agnès. Melzi wiped his brow.

"It started with a spark from the forge," he said. "Before we could do a thing about it, all the wood shavings were alight." Agnès brushed ash from her hair and looked around at the carnage. The flying machine was gone and the giant catapult lay in ruins. Melzi started to count the workers as they filed past. When he got to the last few, he seemed agitated.

"Someone is missing," he said. "There should be one more."

"Where is Madame Moreau?" called out Sister Excelsior. "Has anyone seen her?"

"She was right behind me a moment ago," said Sister Liwet. Without a word to anyone, Bertrand spun around and hurried back along the path towards the barn, calling out for Madame Moreau as he went. Moments later, he emerged from behind the blackened ruins, holding her in his arms like a limp rag doll. She was covered in thick ash and soot, and blood trickled from a gash in her leg. Everyone gathered around.

"I need a bandage to stop the bleeding," said Bertrand, laying Madame Moreau down beside the path. Sister Liwet tore a strip from the hem of her pinafore and held it out.

"And water," said Bertrand, stemming the flow of blood with the rag. Roland was back in no time with his bucket brimming over. Washing away the ash and blood from Madame Moreau's injured leg, Bertrand bound the wound tightly. Lifting her in his arms, and holding her close, he set off for the manor house with everyone following close behind.

When she saw them coming, Maturina opened the doors wide, and Bertrand carried Madame Moreau inside. With sombre faces, everyone watched and waited for Doctor Leveque to arrive. Pepin was frantic and wanted to see his mama. The twins were crying hysterically. Sister Liwet did all she could to console them and held the twins tightly in her arms as they cried out. Very soon, a black carriage clattered into the courtyard and Monsieur Leveque, the physician, got out. He rushed up the steps into Le Cloux and Maturina closed the door behind him.

Waiting and watching, no one uttered a word. When the physician finally came out, everyone gathered around, eager to hear what he had to say.

"Her injuries are not severe," said the doctor. "She will make a full recovery." Maturina stepped out and beckoned for the children to come inside.

"Your mama is waiting," she said. As Pepin and the twins ran up the steps to see her, Agnès felt the tears well up in her eyes.

"This is all my fault," she said. Sister Cathetel put her arms around her.

"You mustn't blame yourself," she said.

"But it would never have happened if I hadn't asked you all to come," said Agnès.

"She wanted to help," said Sister Excelsior. "We all did—we knew what it meant to you."

"It couldn't be helped," said Sister Ecanas. "It was an accident."

"That's not true," Agnès insisted. "It was all my fault." She pulled away and ran off sobbing. Retracing her steps, she headed back to the ruins of the flying machine. Her heart ached as she passed by piles of smouldering ashes. The blaze had devoured everything, consuming all but the iron tools and fittings that it hadn't the stomach to digest. Agnès gazed up into the trees, where fragments of silk hung from the branches like thin blue leaves. As she surveyed the awful scene, dark clouds gathered around her. In the gloom and despair of the moment, she heard a voice. It was Roland.

"Don't feel so bad," he said.

"It's all over," said Agnès, wiping the tears from her eyes. "The Falco has gone and the Birdman's dream is over."

"Don't say that," said Roland. "The Master wouldn't want

you to feel bad." Agnès turned away.

"I only ever wanted to see him get better," she said. "I wanted him to be happy."

She wandered off into the woods, in search of a place to be alone. The smell of smoke lingered in the air, and ash drifted down through the branches. Finding a log to sit on, Agnès unclasped her father's bag and took out his journal. She opened it up and began to read. It was the day that he and his comrades had set off in canoes along the shores of the Great South Sea.

October Twenty-fifth 1514

As we rowed along the shores of this vast country we encountered a dreadful storm from the West that blew in across the ocean. The great hurricane descended upon us with terrible force, stirring the sea into a boiling cauldron. Fernando Suarez and I have been separated from the others.

It is nothing but a miracle that we are still alive. At one time, I thought I might never take another breath and would drown in the depths. After the storm abated, Fernando and I were cast upon an unknown shore. Our little canoe has suffered greatly and is barely able to float.

Agnès could only imagine how awful it had been for her father, his dreams dashed on that lonely beach. As she read on, things only got worse.

October Twenty-Sixth 1514

At first light of day, we discovered the wretched bodies of our comrades and their broken canoe washed up on the beach. We dug graves and honoured each brave soul with a simple cross. Our damaged canoe has been ravaged by the storm, but we will endeavour to repair it and will continue south on our journey in search of the Mountain Palace.

"Why didn't he give up?" Agnès puzzled. "What made him keep going?" She turned the page and read how her papa and Signor Suarez had paddled along the rocky coastline of the great southern ocean for many days before coming ashore where a tribe of friendly natives had taken them in. She read of the villager's hospitality—how they had cared for the two men and helped them repair their battered canoe.

November Third 1514

*Leaving our canoe in a rocky cove, we climbed
to the top of a high ridge and discovered a fertile
valley inhabited by the most welcoming tribe
we ever encountered. Never before have I known
such kindness nor met such a happy people. The
natives practice many traditions and customs.
They cover their bodies in a paste of red berries
and hang medallions of gold and silver from
their ears and necks.*

*After boiling the stems of forest plants, they
prepare a noxious poison in which they dip their
hunting spears and arrows. The potion is most
effective and can stupefy a fully grown beast or a
large fish. Fernando and I have been sheltered in
a very agreeable cabana and have been fed wild
game of every sort. It will be a sorry day for us
both when we take our leave.*

*We are able to communicate with the tribal
elders by way of simple signs and gestures
and have attempted to learn the basics of their
language.*

Agnès read how the natives had helped the two men on their way to the City of Gold in the mountains by carrying provisions for them as far as the next valley.

November Fourteenth 1514

With our canteens full, and enough food to last us the week, Fernando and I took our bearings and set off on foot through the jungles. The locals say it is no more than four days journey from here to the Golden Palace. Our spirits have been lifted, knowing that the City of El Rey Dorado is now within our reach.

The fate of Signor Balboa and the others remains a mystery to us. We fear that perhaps they have all perished in the storm or that they are cast upon another shore.

Amazed by his sheer determination, Agnès felt proud to think that her papa had not abandoned his quest, despite the storm and being separated from the others. It was then that she knew what she must do. Giving up on the flying machine was not an option. She must find a way to carry on.

30

The Birdman was fully aware of the Falco's awful fate. Melzi had told him, but he listened intently to Agnès anyway. Sitting by his bedside, she recounted all that had happened—how the Falco, and everything with it, had been destroyed by fire. Gazing through the open window, the Birdman slowly drew breath and sighed deeply.

"I once spent many weeks on a very large wall painting, only to find that my paint mixture was of the wrong type," he said. "No sooner had the paint dried, than it cracked and peeled away from the plaster. My beautiful masterpiece lay on the floor like fallen autumn leaves."

"I suppose you wished you had never bothered to paint it in the first place," said Agnès.

"Perhaps at first, but then I worked out a way to improve the paint," said the Birdman. "And I set about the task all over again."

"So you didn't feel like giving up?"

"At times," said the Birdman. "But with my new paint recipe, I had fresh hope."

"Was the new painting as good as your first one?"

"Better," said the Birdman. "I was never entirely satisfied with my original efforts, so it gave me the chance to put things right."

"Do you think we should start over again with the flying machine and the crossbow?" Agnès asked. The Birdman didn't hesitate for one moment.

"Without question," he said. "You must."

"But how?" said Agnès. "All your plans were destroyed in the fire." The Birdman pointed to the door that led to his room of books and drawings.

"You'll find fresh paper in the cabinet by the far wall," he said. "And something to draw with on the table." Agnès went off and came back a few moments later with a large sheet of paper and a drawing stick. She handed them to the Birdman. Without delay, he set about sketching shapes and lines with swift strokes, pouring out his thoughts onto the page.

"All the plans are in here," he said, tapping his forehead. His drawing was of a slender wing. "See how the upper surface is curved, just like a bird's," he went on. Agnès looked over the drawing and listened as the Birdman explained how the Falco's wings must be fashioned in the same way. Drafting out his grand design, he drew the tail and described how it should be free to bend like a ship's rudder. When he had finished, he handed the drawing to Agnès. "Now go and get the others to help you," he said. Agnès looked the Birdman in the eyes.

"I won't let you down this time," she said. The Birdman smiled.

"Persistere!" he said. "Good fortune favours the determined

mind." Rolling up the Birdman's drawing, Agnès tucked it under her arm and set off to find the others.

Pepin was wandering about down by the blackened ruins of the old barn when Agnès finally caught up with him. He was picking through bits of charred wood and the scorched remains of tools and implements. The whole area was a boneyard of disembodied metal hoops, springs, coils, hooks, brackets and hinges. Agnès told him what the Birdman had said about not giving up and showed him the drawing.

"I knew he would know what to do," said Pepin.

"We have to try again," said Agnès. "We were so close last time." Pepin took little convincing. All they had to do now was persuade the others.

Melzi was sitting at his easel in the downstairs salon, staring at a drawing of a flower. Agnès hurried over and showed him the Birdman's drawing.

"Look," she said, pointing. "These are our new plans for the Falco." Melzi never even glanced at the sheet of paper.

"You can't be serious," he said.

"Of course," said Agnès. "You didn't think I would give up that easily did you?" Melzi shook his head.

"But there's nothing left. It's all gone."

"We have the carpenters and the sisters," said Agnès. "And I'm sure Bertrand and Roland will come back."

"It would take weeks," said Melzi, shaking his head. "Months even." Agnès pointed to the Birdman's drawing.

"The curve of the wing is the most important thing," she said, remembering what the Birdman had told her. Melzi frowned.

"Didn't you hear me?" he said. "It can't be done."

"We built the flying machine once before didn't we?" said Agnès. "So we can do it again."

"You can if you like," said Melzi. "But not me—count me out." Agnès rolled up the Birdman's drawing.

"Come on, Pepin," she said, heading for the door. "We don't need Melzi anymore—we can do this on our own."

Sitting on a log by the pond, Agnès and Pepin looked over the Birdman's plans carefully. They guessed at the cost of all the materials they would need to rebuild the flying machine and made a list of tools that had to be replaced. After writing down every expense on a scrap of paper, Agnès totalled it all up.

"That's nearly nine hundred ecus," said Pepin, his eyes wide at the sight of such a large sum.

"Leave it to me," said Agnès. "I can get it."

Stuffing the list in her pocket, she got up and set off for the Treasurer's House, determined to show Melzi how wrong he was. They would build the flying machine, and it would be no thanks to him.

The tall chimneys of the treasury reached high above the rooftops. Agnès climbed the steps leading up to the main entrance and waited in the foyer to be seen. Monsieur Borean, the treasurer, was entering a transaction in a fat ledger that lay open on his desk when she went in. She sat down with her list.

"I'd like to withdraw one thousand ecus," said Agnès, taking out her certificate of account. Monsieur Borean took hold of the document.

"There is a problem with this account," he said.

"A problem?" said Agnès, shaking her head. The treasurer sat back in his chair.

"Marshal Lupus came to see me the other day," he explained. "He told me you had paid one hundred ecus to set a prisoner free."

"That's right," said Agnès. "What of it?"

"Well, he seemed very suspicious," said Monsieur Borean. "He asked me how you had obtained such a large sum of money."

"You told him about my certificate, didn't you?" said Agnès. "That the money is lawfully mine." Monsieur Borean nodded.

"So what's the problem?" said Agnès. The treasurer held up the document.

"The Marshal quite rightly pointed out that we have no proof that you are, indeed, the same Agnès Desmarais named in this certificate."

"Well of course I am," said Agnès. "Who else would I be?"

"Unless you have proof of it," said Monsieur Borean, "then we can only assume that you are an imposter."

"An imposter!" railed Agnès, getting up from her chair. "Of course I'm not an imposter."

"Then I trust you can show me a certificate to prove it," said the treasurer. Agnès shifted awkwardly.

"You have three days to furnish me with such a document," said Monsieur Borean. "Otherwise, I will be obliged to transfer the remainder of your eighty-thousand ecus to the King's coffers."

"Three days?" said Agnès. "Why three days?"

"Those are the rules," said the Treasurer. "The law is very clear on the matter and also demands that you pay back the money you have already been given." Agnès was left speechless. She stared down at the list of things she needed to rebuild the Falco. Dazed and bewildered, she got up and headed for the door, brushing past the clerk on her way out.

31

Wandering through the narrow passages and alleyways of Amboise, Agnès felt confused and angry. She was unable to figure out where to go or what to do next. There was no point asking the Reverend Mother for help. She knew nothing of her life before her arrival at the convent four years ago. Agnès had no aunts, uncles, grandparents or cousins that she could ask. There seemed to be no way of sorting it all out. When her feet ached, and her legs grew weary, she sat beside the riverbank and gazed upstream. She watched minnows, flicking their tails as they struggled against the flow of the Loire. In much the same way, it was as if some unseen force was thwarting her every effort.

As she sat there, Agnès looked at the boats moored along the quayside. Reaching into her papa's bag, she took out his journal. She opened it up to the day he first set off on his journey from Amboise.

"I worked my passage aboard the Espadon to the port of Saint-Nazaire." he had written. "Life at Muides is no longer bearable after the death of my beloved wife, Céline." Agnès stared down at the page. She read the words over and over again.

"That's it!" she said, realising what she must do. The journal held the answer all along. She now knew exactly where to go to find the proof she needed.

Excitedly, Agnès got up from the riverbank and hurried along the riverside to where the boatmen were busy lifting barrels and boxes onto their vessels.

"Where are you sailing to?" she asked one. The boatman wiped his brow with a rag.

"Downstream to Tours," he said, pointing. Agnès ran along to the next boat.

"I need to get to the village of Muides," she said. "Do you know it?" The boatman nodded.

"I'll pass that way tomorrow," he said. Agnès searched in her bag for her money pouch. She tipped out all her coins and counted them. There was enough to pay for her passage to Muides and for food to eat along the way. She thought about Pepin and knew that he would wonder where she had gone. Turning to the boatman, she asked him how much longer it would be before he set sail.

"As soon as I've loaded this lot, I'll be on my way," said the boatman. Agnès hadn't got time to tell Pepin. She had only three days to get to the place of her birth and find proof of who she was.

The Bretonne was a single-masted, flat bottomed riverboat, heading upstream to Orleans. Agnès paid four sous for her passage and climbed aboard. She sat on a barrel of salt fish, watching gulls that trailed in its wake as it sailed away. Squawking and swooping, the birds snatched at scraps of fish that the boatman had swept from the deck.

Cutting through the water like a proud swan, the Bretonne slipped gracefully past fields and woodlands on its journey. It passed by ancient castles, tiny hamlets, rocky outcrops and grassy sandbanks. Twisted roots and branches drifted by, and the vessel's broad white sail billowed in the breeze as it sailed all afternoon and into the evening.

When the sun sank low in the sky, the boatman said they would soon be approaching the town of Blois where they would moor for the night. He would be setting off again at seven in the morning and told Agnès not to be late.

Clambering ashore, Agnès went in search of the coaching inn, where she had been told she could get a good meal and a place to sleep. As she walked along the quayside, she caught sight of two older boys, leaning against a ramshackle hut of rickety timbers. The boys looked dirty and scruffy. She knew their sort only too well.

Holding on to her father's bag tightly, she made her way along the narrow thoroughfare. When she glanced around, the two boys had gone. With quickening steps, she hurried on her way. When she reached the next alleyway, however, the same two boys stood blocking the way ahead.

Agnès stopped dead in her tracks.

"What's in the bag?" demanded one of the boys. Agnès

stepped back. She gripped her bag tightly.

"Well, come on—hand it over!" said the boy. As he tried to grab it off her, Agnès pushed him away and made a run for it. She darted down a narrow alley and ran across a cobbled square. She could hear the boys following after her. When she spotted the open door of a small chapel, she dashed over and darted inside. Hiding behind a pillar, Agnès tried not to make a sound. With her heart racing, she stood with her back to the stone column, listening for voices and footsteps. After several minutes, hearing neither, she finally stepped back out. She went over to the doorway and looked across the cobbled square. The boys were nowhere to be seen. Weary from the whole ordeal, she closed the chapel door and laid out on a long wooden bench with her head resting on her papa's travel bag. There seemed little point in going back out. The boys might only be waiting around the corner—and then what would she do?

32

Agnès woke up with a crick in her neck, a bitter taste in her mouth, and a mark on her arm where the buckle of her father's bag had left its impression. As the church bells rang out in the belfry high above, she counted seven chimes.

"Seven!" she gasped, leaping up.

In a mad panic, Agnès hurried over to the chapel door and dashed out. She ran across the cobbled square, along the thoroughfare, and back towards the waterfront. When she got there, the boatman was hoisting his sails.

"Wait, don't go!" she called out. The boatman looked around.

"I told you not to be late," he said.

"It's only just seven," said Agnès, leaping from the quayside onto the deck of the Bretonne. She grabbed a rope to steady herself and sat down beside a barrel of fish.

"Another five minutes and I would have been gone," said the boatman. He leaned on the rudder and steered from shore.

With the wind in its sails, the Bretonne set off upstream. Once the vessel was on its way, the boatman set up a small griddle and started to fry up a pan of fish. As the pan sizzled, Agnès asked him what he knew of Muides.

"Not a lot," said the boatman. "It's hardly much of a place." He served up two plates of fish and handed one to Agnès. As she sat, picking out the bones, she asked where she might find a record of all the people born in Muides.

"The church is where I would go," said the boatman. "Why do you ask?" Agnès explained that Muides was where she thought she had been born; it was where her father came from.

"He sailed away four years ago," she said.

"What was his name?" asked the boatman.

"Jacques Desmarais."

"Never heard of him," said the boatman, shaking his head. "I see a lot of travellers pass this way."

When she had finished eating, Agnès scraped her plate clean and washed it in the flowing waters of the Loire. Later that morning, when the sun was high, the Bretonne approached a tiny hamlet surrounded by marshlands. The boatman pointed beyond the grassy banks to a tall spire. "That's the place you're looking for," he said. Agnès got up and steadied herself against the mast.

"How do I get over the marshes?" she said.

"You'll find a path that leads to a bridge," said the boatman. "Follow it to the church." He pulled on the rudder and steered the Bretonne close to the bank. Clambering over the side, Agnès lowered herself into the water. She waded through the muddy shallows, pushing aside tall reeds and rushes as she made her way to shore. She turned and waved back as the boat sailed away.

After crossing over the bridge, Agnès came to a path that led beside a row of small cottages. Wisps of smoke drifted up from their chimneys. A dog barked and a woman peered out from her window as she walked by. When she came to the church, she tried the door. It was open. Clutching her father's bag, she went inside and slowly made her way past the stations of the cross. Standing by the altar, lighting candles, was a grey-haired man in a long black robe.

"Are you the priest?" said Agnès. The man looked around.

"Yes, I'm Father Legrand," he said.

"I need your help," said Agnès.

"Go on," said the priest, lighting another candle. Agnès asked if there was a book with the names of all the people born in Muides. Father Legrand nodded.

"Why do you ask?"

"I think I was born here."

"You don't know for sure?"

"I know I used to live here with my papa," said Agnès. She explained about her father, Jacques Desmarais, and his fate in the Americas. Father Legrand listened intently. He walked over to a large book by the church altar. Opening it up, he ran his finger down the page.

"I think this is what you're looking for," he said, showing the book to Agnès. Written in black ink, Agnès could see her name and the date of her birth.

"That's me," she said. Father Legrand nodded.

"It is you, Agnès," he said.

"Do you remember me?" Agnès asked. Father Legrand nodded.

"There's no mistaking who you are—you look very much like your mother."

"You remember her too?"

"I remember the day you were born," said Father Legrand. "No one thought you would survive. Your father called me over to perform the baptism before the day was out." Agnès looked down at the page. Written beside her own name were the names of her parents, Jacques and Céline Desmarais.

"Your Mother was very brave," said Father Legrand. "She loved you and your father very much."

"I wish she was still here," said Agnès softly.

"Perhaps she is," said Father Legrand. "I would say she lives on in you."

"I remember her singing," said Agnès.

"Yes, she was always singing," said Father Legrand. We called her the Nightingale of the Marshes."

Agnès recalled the dream she had—seeing her mother, sitting on the cottage doorstep—peeling apples—with a bright rainbow of colours all around her.

"Why did she die?" said Agnès. "No one ever told me." Father Legrand sat on a pew.

"She suffered from marsh fever," he explained. "It had been a very warm year and many died from the ague."

"Father Legrand, I need your help," said Agnès. "I need a certificate to prove who I am."

"Why is it so important?" asked the priest. Agnès hesitated. She wasn't sure she should mention anything about Signor Suarez and her father's riches. What might Father Legrand think of such worldly wealth?

"I'm thinking of joining the Minimes Convent," she said.

"Yes, of course," said the priest. "That is a very devout and saintly thing for a young girl like you to do. I wholly approve." Fetching a sheet of parchment, he rested on the altar and copied out a certificate stating that Agnès was indeed born and baptised at Muides on April the twenty-fifth, fifteen hundred and seven. Then, taking a lighted candle, he dripped hot wax onto the paper and pressed it with the Seal of Saint Jerome. Wafting the document dry, he handed it to Agnès.

"Thank you," she said.

Walking back along the aisle to the chapel door, Father Legrand led the way outside to a small wooden cross beside a yew tree. Kneeling by the grave, Agnès reached out and traced her finger over the name of Céline Desmarais. She picked a handful of yellow flowers and laid them by the cross. As a gentle breeze blew through the trees, Father Legrand pointed along a narrow track that led over the marshes.

"Your father's cottage is still there," he said. "The place

has been empty ever since you left." Agnès thanked Father Legrand and set off, clutching her certificate. She followed the narrow path over the marshlands. The way was soft and springy underfoot. An earthy smell filled the air and Agnès thought how familiar it all seemed. Long-forgotten memories came flooding back as she walked through the cotton grass and clumps of yellow gorse. She could hear the warbling of birds and the buzz of bees. Watery brown pools rippled as insects danced on its surface.

Up ahead, stood a small abandoned cottage. Its thatch of dried reeds and turf was completely overgrown with moss and creepers. A stork had built its nest on the chimney top. Agnès walked around the outside of the cottage and tried the door. The hinges were stiff and it wouldn't budge. When she pulled open the shutter of a small window, a startled bird flew out and flapped off over the marshes. Brushing aside a tangle of cobwebs, she looked in.

Floorboards were thick with dust. Cracked plaster hung from the walls and fireplace. Agnès could see a nest up in the rafters and could hear the chirp of tiny hatchlings. When she climbed through the window, the chicks fell silent. She looked around at what remained of her childhood home. There was a broken chair, a rickety table and an embroidered picture of a songbird on the wall. As she stepped back, her foot met with something hard. She turned and looked down. It was a small crib. Kneeling beside the wooden cot, Agnès reached inside

and picked up a dirty rag doll. She held it tightly and rocked
it back and forth.

"I remember you," she said, tears welling up in her eyes.
"You belonged to me—you were mine."

33

As the bells of Saint Jerome rang out in the distance, Agnès knew her time was fast running out. She hurried back along the marshy path, flanked by gorse and heather. She passed by the church and the cottages—with the barking dog and the nosy woman looking out. At last, she arrived at the riverside where she sat amongst the rushes, waiting and watching for a boat to come along. When a white canvas sail appeared around the bend, Agnès waved the vessel to shore and offered the boatman a silver cob for her passage to Amboise.

"I can take you as far as Blois," said the boatman. "That's as far as I'm going." Agnès climbed aboard and sat amongst piles of woollen fleeces and crates of turnips. As the boat sailed along, she watched fishermen along the banks, hauling in their lines. She waved at a ploughman, watering his horses in the shallows. The hours passed slowly. As the sky turned hazy in the glow of the evening, the boat finally arrived back at the town of Blois.

Climbing out onto the quayside, Agnès went from boat to boat until she found one that was due to sail for Amboise early the next morning. It was called the Maid of Orleans. She then set off in search of the coaching inn, keeping a watchful eye on the road ahead. Walking briskly, she looked up as the first stars began to appear. She thought about her dear mother, Céline Desmarais, and imagined her standing on some far celestial shore, waiting for her papa's Spanish caravel to come along. She pictured them both together again, watching down from that heavenly place.

"Perhaps they have been watching all along," she thought.

The inn was not far away now, and Agnès could hear the clink of tankards and the sound of laughter inside.

When she felt a tug from behind, Agnès spun around and saw the same two boys that had followed her the night before. One of them snatched at her papa's bag. She tried to hold on, but this time the boy wrestled it from her shoulder and ran off with it. The other boy shoved her to the ground.

Agnès yelled as the boys ran off. She tried to get up, but her ankle was twisted and her hand was bleeding from the fall. Tears welled up in her eyes. After all she had been through to get her certificate, she couldn't let those two wretches get away. Remembering where she had first seen them—beside the ramshackle hut—she slowly got to her feet and limped back towards the quayside.

A lone fisherman, tying up his nets, was the only soul about when she got there. Agnès went over and asked him if he had seen two boys. The fisherman shook his head. When she got to the ramshackle hut, she looked inside, but there was no sign of them. Sitting on a barrel, rubbing her swollen ankle, Agnès watched a small mouse as it scurried over the cobbles, stopping to nibble at grains of wheat and barley between the cracks.

When she heard voices and laughing, she hid behind the barrel. The voices grew louder and she could see the two boys heading her way. One of them was carrying her papa's bag. When they got to the quayside, the boys crouched low beside a pile of old crates. Unbuckling the bag, they tipped it up and emptied everything onto the cobbles.

"What's this?" said one, thumbing through the pages of her papa's journal. He tossed it to one side and unrolled her certificate.

"More worthless rubbish," said the boy. Agnès watched as they went through all her things. When they got to her money pouch, the two thieving urchins grew more excited. They shared out the coins then got up and walked off, laughing. When the boys had gone, Agnès hobbled over and gathered up her things. She dusted off her father's journal, rolled up her certificate, and put everything back in the bag. She then wandered off along the riverside in search of a place to curl up for the night. With the last of her money gone, she had no way of paying for a room at the inn or her passage back to Amboise.

The next morning, Agnès stood by the quayside, watching with a heavy heart as the Maid of Orleans sailed off without her. With her ankle still swollen, every step made her wince as she set off along the road back to Amboise. She tried not to think about it and did her best to block out the pain. The road was long and winding. By midday, she was barely halfway there.

Sitting on a log by the roadside to rest her feet, she heard the clatter of hooves and cartwheels. When she looked back along the path, she spotted a hay wagon coming her way. Getting up, she waved to the driver.

"Where are you going?" she called out. The man reined his horse and the wagon came to a halt.

"Limeray," he said. "Hop on the back if you want a ride." Agnès clambered aboard. She sat amongst the hay, gazing up at the shifting clouds as the wagon set off. When she closed her eyes, she felt her aches and pains melt away with each passing mile. Despite her setback, she felt pleased with herself for not giving up. The loss of a few coins was nothing really. More importantly, she had managed to get back her certificate and the journal. Nothing else seemed to matter.

When the hay wagon reached Limeray, Agnès climbed down and continued along the north bank of the Loire on foot. She walked along the narrow path for another hour before the walls and ensigns of the Royal Château finally came into view. As she passed by the limestone cliffs, on the opposite bank of the river, she spotted the entrance to her cavern hideaway. It seemed so tiny, perched up there above the Loire. Further along, she could see the Minimes Convent and the Château with its ensigns fluttering in the breeze.

When, at last, she reached the bridge of seven arches, Agnès crossed over to the other side. Carriages and horses clattered along the thoroughfare. She waited to get across as market traders crisscrossed back and forth with barrows and carts at the end of a busy day. Clutching her certificate, she hurried up the steps of the Treasurer's House. When she got to the top, however, the doors were locked and the windows were shuttered.

Agnès stared blankly. Like the walls of a great fortress, the door was an impenetrable barrier that she couldn't break through. Her best efforts hadn't been enough. Monsieur Borean had granted her three days to prove who she was, and she had failed.

Flopping down on the steps of the Treasurer's House, Agnès felt utterly beaten and exhausted. She looked out across the empty market square and watched an old beggar who was scavenging for discarded bits of fruit and vegetables. When she heard someone calling out her name, she looked around. It was Pepin.

"Agnès where have you been?" he said, rushing up the steps to greet her. Agnès wiped her eyes.

"It hardly matters now," she said. "What about you?"

"I've been at Le Cloux," said Pepin, "helping with the flying machine." Agnès stared.

"You've been doing what?"

"You heard—we've been rebuilding the Falco."

"But how?" said Agnès. "You needed my money."

"We couldn't wait," said Pepin. "Melzi has sorted it all out while you've been away."

"Melzi!" Agnès blurted. "But he refused to help."

"Well, he changed his mind," said Pepin, "He wants to help now, and the Birdman has paid for everything."

"I have to go and see," said Agnès, getting to her feet. Pepin shook his head.

"Not now," he said. "Everyone has gone home for the day. I'll show you tomorrow—you won't believe what we've done."

34

Back at the cottage, Pepin's mama was so pleased to see Agnès and to know that she was alright. Agnès was happy to see that Madame Moreau's injuries were healing fast and that she was able to walk again.

"Bertrand has been coming round every day to check on me," said Madame Moreau. "He is very kind and helps out no end." Agnès sat in the parlour by the window and did her best to explain where she had been. She recounted everything that had happened to her since she had gone away. She showed her swollen ankle, and Madame Moreau wrapped a bandage around it.

"We both need a little care and attention don't we?" she said. "It's a good job we have each other."

The next morning, Agnès and Pepin set off for the manor house with a basket of bread and cheese that Madame Moreau had packed up for the day.

When they arrived, a large wagon—pulled by heavy horses and loaded with timber—stood by the gates of Le Cloux. Workers were busy carrying long lengths of yew and oak into the courtyard, and Hugo was showing them where they should stack it all.

"What's all this?" asked Agnès.

"It's for the flying machine," said Hugo. "Melzi's orders."

Following Pepin down to the ruins of the old barn, Agnès went to see what was going on.

"Where have you been?" called out Melzi when he saw her coming. Agnès frowned.

"Never mind me—what about you?" she said. "You said you would have nothing to do with the flying machine."

"I thought it over," said Melzi. "I changed my mind—come and see." Grabbing Agnès by the arm, he led her past the blackened ruins of the barn and into a clearing where a large pavilion of striped canvas had been erected. It was high and wide, like a gala marquee—held taut with ropes and wooden stakes.

"What do you think?" said Melzi. "We're building the Falco in here." Inside the pavilion, the flying machine was already well underway. The framework was much as it had been when she stumbled on the Birdman's little factory for the first time. Long workbenches had been set out with pots of glue, tar and beeswax. There were bolts of cloth, needles and thread, brushes, rope and twine. The Birdman's plans were pinned up on an easel. Agnès walked over and examined them carefully.

"I've been talking with the Master," said Melzi, "and we've made some changes to the plans."

"What are those marks?" said Agnès, pointing to an intricate pattern of circles and squares that Melzi had drawn.

"It shows the carpenters where to hollow out the wood to make it lighter," said Melzi. "The Master says that a bird's bones are not solid, like ours—they're full of holes." Hearing voices behind her, Agnès turned and saw Bertrand and Roland heading over.

"You came back!" she said.

"Of course," said Bertrand. "This is the best job we've ever had."

"The Sisters are here too," said Roland. "I've just seen them arrive from the convent."

Very soon, the marquee was full of workers, all of them ready and eager to carry on where they had left off. The carpenters and blacksmiths had brought along their own tools. Out in the open, a new forge had been set up, away from the marquee.

"Well, what are we waiting for," said Agnès, heartened by everything she had seen and heard. "Let's get going."

The little band soon got to work. They sawed and carved. They stitched and sang. Agnès and Pepin helped too. They cut and tied ropes, mixed glue and fetched whatever was needed. Roland taught them to splice the ends of ropes to stop them from fraying. Bertrand set to work on a new eagle-head carving, just like the last one. Using strips of dry fish skin, he taught them to rub the wood until it felt as smooth as polished marble.

Later on, Agnès went to see the Birdman. She told him

about her journey to Muides and what she had gone there for. She explained about finding proof of her birth—and about missing the treasurer's deadline.

"I was too late," she said. "And now all my father's money will now go to the King's coffers." The Birdman reached out and took Agnès by the hand.

"Don't you fret," he said. "Monsieur Borean is a good friend of mine. I'll see to it that you get what is rightfully yours."

"You would do that?" said Agnès, her face lighting up. The Birdman smiled.

"That's what friends are for," he said. "They help one another, don't they?"

That very day, the Master wrote a letter to Monsieur Borean, explaining Agnès had not returned within the allotted time. He put her certificate of birth in the envelope. Before the end of the next day, he had received a letter back from the Treasurer. It stated that the matter had been dealt with, and Agnès was free to withdraw her money whenever she liked.

As each day passed and the workers toiled, Agnès looked for better ways to control the Falco's movements. Along with Pepin and Melzi, she experimented with a lighter and more efficient mechanism for twisting the tail without using heavy pulleys. With her money, she bought a notebook and a writing stylus that she carried with her wherever she went. As the experiments continued, she sketched and wrote what happened.

Watching the birds in the garden, she marvelled at how they could take to the skies so easily, working with the wind to rise up. She watched the motions of their wing and drew their various shapes. Sometimes, she would sit and talk with Pepin as he whittled with a sharp knife, carving bits of wood into little birds and creatures. In her notebook, Agnès recorded the Falco's progress. Each evening, by the light of her lamp, she would write what had happened that day.

Tuesday 22nd April 1519

Spent the morning testing new ways to twist the wings. Despite all of Bertrand's hard work, five of the wing struts broke and had to be made over again. The Sisters have set to work on a stronger harness and straps for the flyer.

Wednesday 23rd April 1519

Spent the afternoon in the study, searching the Birdman's books for more ideas. Melzi has been strutting about like a chicken in a barnyard, inspecting the work and giving out orders. This evening I was sure I saw Magellan fly over the manor house. I am certain he knows what we are doing.

Thursday 24th April 1519

Went to Amboise with Anne to buy more horse-glue and beeswax. There is never enough to keep the workers supplied. Maturina cooked and baked all morning. Best of all were her beef dumplings and almond tarts.

Friday 25th April 1519

We were all so busy splitting willows that I nearly forgot that today is my birthday. The Birdman gave me a surprise gift. Inside the box, was the silver ball with the little songbird that flaps and sings. He said he wants me to have it and told me to always keep it safe.

35

The Falco rose like a phoenix from the ashes of disaster. It grew into a thing of beauty, with the sleekest of wings, a tail that fanned out, and Bertrand's eagle head at the helm. Whenever she passed by, Agnès would run her hand over its silky wings and polished struts.

One morning, before the others arrived, she was down by the pavilion when she noticed a large crow, perched on the branch of a tree, looking down at her.

"Magellan, is that you?" she said. She wasn't exactly sure at first. When the crow cawed and flapped to the ground by her feet, Agnès was certain of it.

"What do you think?" she said, pointing at the flying machine in the pavilion. "Have you ever seen a bird like it?" Magellan hopped over to the Falco and pecked at its lower struts. Agnès reached into her pocket and took out one of Maturina's curd tarts. She broke it up and scattered crumbs on the ground.

"That's what I like about you," she said. "You're so predictable."

When Melzi came over from the manor house, he brought news that the Master was feeling well enough to inspect the flying machine for himself. Monsieur Leveque, the physician, was pleased with his recovery and gave his consent, on condition that he didn't try to lift any tools.

Later that morning, with Maturina there to steady him, the Birdman walked into the Pavilion on shaky legs. When he saw Agnès standing by the Falco, a broad smile spread across his face. He slowly made his way over. When he gazed up at the flying machine, his eyes lit up.

"It's just as I dreamt it would be," he said.

"I'm glad you approve," said Melzi. The Birdman inspected the wings carefully. Their surfaces were gently curved. A skin of blue silk had been stretched tightly over them and felt stiff to the touch.

"We made it as tight as a drum," said Agnès, pressing down on the fabric.

"Do all the controls work as they should?" said the Birdman. Melzi pulled on a lever. As he did so, the wings twisted. He pulled another and the tail turned from side to side like the rudder of a ship.

"We can control every part," said Agnès.

"Eccellente," said the Birdman. When he grabbed a lever to try for himself, Maturina reached out to stop him.

"Remember what the physician said—you mustn't overdo it," she told him. The Birdman frowned.

"Fiddlesticks!" he said. "I never felt better." Agnès turned to Maturina.

"What do you think of the Falco?" she asked.

"It's magnificent," said Maturina.

"That's it," said the Birdman. "We shall call it the Magnifico Falco." Maturina took the old man by the arm.

"It's time you rested," she said. "You have been up long enough."

"I suppose we mustn't hold up the workers," said the Master. "We don't want to get in the way."

Back at the manor house, later on, Agnès, Pepin and Melzi sat at the kitchen table with a plate of oatcakes between them, mulling over the next part of the plan.

"We need to decide when the flight is going to take place," said Agnès. Melzi suggested that the flying machine should be launched from the Château wall. It was the highest point with a clear line of sight down to the manor house.

"I say we go up there now," he said, "to check how strong the wind is blowing."

With lamps burning brightly, everyone made their way down the narrow steps beneath the cellar and set off along the underground passage that led to the Château. Agnès hadn't been back that way since Anne showed her around the palace. The passage was cold and damp. Melzi's voice echoed along the walls as he called back for the others to keep up. When they reached the foot of the tower, they all hung up their lamps and climbed the steps to the castle wall. Passing by the guards, they walked along the parapet to the farthest corner.

"A perfect line of sight," said Melzi, pointing to the manor house. "Not a single hindrance." He took out a brassy device from his pocket and held it up. Like a miniature windmill, the instrument spun round and round. Melzi counted the number turns it made and wrote it down in a small notebook.

"If the wind is anything like this, there should be no problem at all," he said.

"So, who will be the one to fly?" said Agnès, looking around at the other two. Melzi put away his windmill device and stared blankly.

"Not me," he said, shaking his head. "There's no way I'm going up there." Agnès didn't like to argue. She knew how Melzi felt after his experience back in Tuscany. Pepin gazed out across the great divide.

"I'll do it," he said. Melzi patted him on the shoulder.

"Good man," he said. "After all, you are the smallest and lightest." Gazing down at the Manor of Le Cloux, Agnès could picture the Birdman's flying machine, soaring through the skies with Pepin at the helm. Melzi was right. He was the one who stood the best chance. She felt disappointed but tried not to show it.

On their way back to the tower, Agnès spotted the King and Queen, outside the Chapel of Saint-Hubert. The Queen was cradling a small infant in her arms. The young prince and princess were chasing around her feet.

"It's a baby boy," said Melzi. "His name is Prince Henri."

225

As Agnès watched the children play, she thought back to her first day at Le Cloux. Prince François and Princess Charlotte had been playing in the garden, and Melzi had been trying to make them sit still. She remembered the Birdman picking up the young prince and whirling him around in the air, telling him to fly like a bird. Those days seemed so long ago. Agnès felt strangely different inside. Like a garden that flowers in the springtime, she sensed that something within her had blossomed and grown.

That evening, in the fading light of her room, Agnès took out her father's journal and read, once more, of the days leading up to his discovery of the City of Gold. The pages were worn and curled up at the edges. She had read the account many times already and almost knew it by heart.

November Eighth 1514

Words cannot describe the comradeship that binds me to Fernando Suarez in our quest. Together we have conquered our fears and are about to reach our final destination.

Through the mountain mists, we gained our

first glimpse of the Golden Palace. As we drew near, the natives hailed us as gods. We were carried with great pomp and ceremony to meet their king. And such a king he was. Adorned in gold from head to toe, even his face and arms shone with a dazzling lustre. Fernando and I were presented with treasures beyond anything we could ever have imagined. The King of El Rey Dorado granted us all that we desired and our quest has not been in vain.

The next morning, Melzi came back from visiting the Master, having agreed a date and time for the Grand Départ. Preparations soon got underway in earnest. The Master wrote dozens of invitations that were immediately dispatched by rider to every peer, duke, marquis and earl for miles around.

The King declared it a day of celebration for all the citizens of Amboise and signed a decree, stating that all the streets were to be kept clear.

Melzi was given the job of planning and arranging the whole thing. He threw himself into it with the greatest attention to detail. Agnès and Pepin had a few ideas of their own. They suggested musicians, fireworks, lots of food and a speech by the Master—if he felt up to it. Melzi drew up all the plans.

There would be a ceremonial unveiling of the Magnifico Falco at the Manor of Le Cloux, followed by a procession along the streets of Amboise. Pepin would then fly down from the eastern wall of the Château to the manor house lawn. It would be his moment of glory, and he would go down in history as *The Boy Who Flew*.

With her money, Agnès bought more fabric from Monsieur Etoffe. She gave it to Madame Moreau and asked her to sew up a new dress for her to wear on the big day. She also helped design a special suit of clothing for Pepin, with padding sewn into every part of it. As the week went by, a feeling of great excitement and anticipation grew. Everyone was now talking about the flight of the Magnifico Falco. It would be a day of triumph and great jubilation.

36

May 2nd 1519

The dawn chorus seemed earlier than usual on the day of the Grand Départ. By the time Agnès arrived at the Manor of Le Cloux, the place was a bustle of activity. She made her way past maids and scullions, all hurrying back and forth to prepare for the arrival of the King and Queen.

The entrance to the pavilion was draped over with a blue velvet curtain. Inside, Pepin was busy helping Bertrand to wipe away morning dew from the wings of the flying machine. Out on the lawn, workers had set up a raised wooden platform. Melzi was going around, checking that enough seats had been set out for all the guests. The silky blue mural of birds—left over from the banquet—now hung from a high scaffold all around the pavilion. The menagerie of brightly painted birds fluttered and flapped in the morning breeze. Musicians struck up a great cacophony of discordant sounds as they tuned their instruments. The Master had spared no expense. Long tables were set out with plates of tasty morsels and platters of fine pastries for all the guests—many of whom had travelled from far-off places, with a promise of a spectacle unlike any other.

By the time the mid-morning bells rang out, the grand pavilion was all set for the arrival of the King and Queen. Agnès was wearing a yellow dress made of fine taffeta that Madame Moreau had sewn up for her. Spotting Anne, seated on the front row, she went over and sat beside her.

Trumpets sounded as the Royal Coach made its grand entrance. The King and Queen were escorted down to the pavilion and took their seats beside the Master. With everyone in place, the Birdman stepped up onto the wooden platform, assisted on either side by royal courtiers. He was dressed in his finest doublet and wrapped in a black fur cloak. After bowing to the King and Queen, he gazed out over the throng.

"This day will bring glory to his Christian Majesty, King François, and all of France," he announced. "As the Great Bird takes flight, praised be the nest where it was born." He raised a hand and gave the signal for the blue velvet curtain to be drawn back, revealing the Magnifico Falco in all its glory. Courtiers immediately set off Chinese firecrackers that shot out great fountains of coloured lights all around the pavilion.

Heralded by trumpets and bugles, and borne aloft by strong arms, the flying machine was lifted up and carried out onto the lawn. It was a thing of beauty. The King got to his feet and applauded. Loud cheers filled the air. When the ovation died away, the Birdman continued his speech.

"Many years ago, I dreamt of building a machine that would enable a person to fly," he went on. "I have spent my whole life striving to discover how it might be done. Thanks to my good friends, Agnès, Pepin and Melzi—and all their noble assistants—it has, at last, become a reality. I trust that my vision and their efforts will be acceptable."

Pepin stepped up onto the platform, wrapped from head to foot in layers of thick woollen clothing, *to cushion his bones in the event of a bumpy landing*, as Melzi put it. The Birdman rested a hand on Pepin's shoulder.

"This young man—the son of Etienne Moreau of Amboise—will be known for evermore as the boy who flew," he said.

"Godspeed the Magnifico Falco," someone cried from the back of the crowd.

"May she come to earth with all the grace of a swan," called out another.

As musicians struck up with resounding strains of pomp and pageantry, Agnès swelled with a tremendous feeling of pride, knowing what they had all achieved.

Once the formalities were over with, strong men set to work harnessing the giant catapult to a team of heavy horses for its final journey to the Château. Others stepped forwards, ready to help carry the flying machine.

"Gather round and lift where you stand," ordered Melzi.

"And be especially careful with the wings."

The band of helpers surrounded the Magnifico Falco. On Melzi's command, they lifted and turned it sideways so that it could be manoeuvred along the path. They carried it slowly as Agnès and Pepin followed on behind, reaching out to steady the wings whenever they tipped and tilted.

The procession crossed over the lawn and advanced towards the courtyard. The Birdman walked alongside with Maturina holding on to his arm. When he reached the manor house gates, his knees started to buckle. He leaned against the gatepost to steady himself and to mop his brow.

"You're in no fit state to go anywhere," said Maturina.

"Nonsense," said the Birdman, "I feel fine." But Maturina would hear none of it.

"I won't let you go another step," she said firmly. The Birdman shook his head.

"Let me be!" he chuntered.

"You can watch the flight from here at Le Cloux," said Maturina, insistently. The Birdman tried to shore himself up and carry on, but Maturina was adamant.

"What's going on?" said Agnès, hurrying over.

"There's a change of plans," said Maturina. "The journey to the Château is too much for the Master."

"But he can't miss the flight," said Agnès. "Not now." Maturina held on to the Master's arm tightly.

"He won't miss a thing," she said. "There's a perfect view

of the Château wall from the window of his study."

When the King received word of the setback, he ordered his courtiers to carry comfy seats up to the study and put them by the open window. He would stay with the Master and watch the flight of the Magnifico Falco with him.

"We'll give you a signal," said Agnès. "A blast of trumpets and wave of a flag." The Birdman said nothing more about it as Maturina led him away, his steps faltering as he went.

Workers now got on with the task of carrying the flying machine to the tower. The way was narrow and it took great skill and care for them to navigate it along the thoroughfare of half-timbered houses. They had to hold it sideways and kept stopping to rest along the way. When they reached the Château wall, men from the barracks stepped up to help. With strong arms and broad shoulders, they lifted the flying machine onto the rampart. Everyone watched anxiously as it teetered beside the tower gates.

"Stop, stop!" Melzi cried out, waving his arms. "The gate isn't wide enough." The workers shuffled back in unison. They eased the Magnifico Falco down and held it steady.

"I have an idea," said Agnès. "Why don't they lift it up on the outside of the wall with ropes." Pepin pointed.

"It looks like they already thought of that," he said. When Agnès looked up, she could see workers, securing pulleys to a long wooden beam at the top of the Château wall. Moments later, thick ropes were being lowered, and others, down below, began looping them around the flying machine. After checking knots and fastenings, they heaved and hauled. Slowly the Magnifico Falco rose up.

Agnès hardly dared breathe as she watched the flying machine being lifted up. Weaving her way through the crowd, she set off up the steps with Pepin and Melzi. Emerging through the low archway at the top of the tower, they were just in time to see the Magnifico Falco being untied from its harness. They followed behind as workers carried it along the Château wall to the eastern corner where the giant crossbow stood waiting.

Once it had been secured to the catapult's mechanism, Melzi went around checking every joint and link to make sure that nothing had worked loose or fallen off along the way.

"It's perfectly fine," he said, pulling down on the wingtips.

"I guess this is it," said Agnès, turning to Pepin. "You'll be back at the manor house long before we get there." Melzi walked along to the corner of the Château wall. Taking out his little wind-measuring device, he held it up. The vanes spun around, and he counted their revolutions. Giving a nod, he slipped the device back in his pocket.

Pepin stepped up to the edge of the precipice and looked down. Agnès expected him to make some sort of speech, but he just stood, like a statue. He didn't say a word.

"Well," she said. "Aren't you going to say something?"

As she watched and waited, Pepin started to sway about.

"Is he all right?" said Melzi, holding out his arms to steady the boy.

"I'm f-fine," Pepin stammered. Agnès could see that he wasn't. All the blood had drained from his face, and he had a far-away look in his eyes. Without another word, Pepin started to topple. Rushing forwards, Agnès reached out to steady him.

"I feel sick!" blurted Pepin, holding his stomach and spluttering. "I can't do it."

37

An enormous crowd had gathered below to watch the flight of the Magnifico Falco. The entire marketplace was packed with excited onlookers, all jostling for the best view.

"Can't you see how sick I am?" moaned Pepin.

"You were fine a few moments ago," said Agnès. Pepin bowed his head.

"I can't do it," he wailed.

"But you have to," Agnès told him. "Everyone is waiting to see you fly." Pepin slumped down.

"I can't," he said. "I'm scared." Agnès stepped forwards.

"Then I'll do it," she said. Melzi saw the look in her eyes.

"You really would, wouldn't you?" he said. Agnès gave a nod.

"I know how everything works," she said.

"Agnès, wait!" said Melzi, grabbing her by the arm. "We need to get you dressed in Pepin's flying suit."

"There's no time for that," said Agnès, pulling her arm away. "Anyway, it wouldn't fit me."

Clambering onto the giant crossbow, she worked her way

between the slender timber framework until she was right inside the belly of the flying machine. Squeezing herself into the tight space between its wings, she fastened the straps around her shoulders. Buckles and knots dug into her sides as she secured the harness. She worked her feet into the stirrups and grabbed the control handles. Pepin just sat there, groaning.

"I'm ready," Agnès called out. Melzi gave a nod.

Strong men heaved and hauled on the gigantic winding handles of the crossbow. Ropes flexed and creaked. As the handles turned, the Magnifico Falco slowly drew back. With every notch, the ropes tightened. Agnès felt a heavy jolt as the locking mechanism clicked into place. Ropes creaked, and the wings of the Magnifico Falco bent and flexed. She felt a restless tug as its wings caught the breeze. With the sun now bursting from behind a cloud, she could see the skeletal frame of the wing through its thin fabric skin.

"Wait a moment!" called out Melzi, clambering up onto the bulwark of the catapult. "I want to check the firing angle one more time." Only when everything was lined up correctly, would he declare the Magnifico Falco ready for launch.

Agnès gripped the controls tightly and checked that her feet were level. She gazed ahead at the manor house in the distance and looked down at the crowd of onlookers. She could see Mother Superior and the sisters from the Minimes Convent. Bertrand and Roland were there too, standing by the water pump with Pepin's mama and the twins, Eva and Ida.

On the steps of the Treasurer's House, she could see Monsieur Borean and his wiry-looking clerk.

When a dark shadow flapped overhead, Agnès looked up and saw Magellan. Swooping down, he landed on the wall by her side. He hobbled along the wall towards her, cawing loudly.

"You're not the only one who can fly, now," Agnès called out to him.

"On my command, release the flying machine," Melzi cried. Goliath, the big African, lifted a heavy hammer above his head, ready to strike the firing latch. Agnès braced herself. When she looked down, her heart leapt. Melzi raised both arms high above his head.

"Vola libero!" he called out at the top of his voice. A flag waved and trumpets sounded. Agnès shut her eyes and gritted her teeth. As Goliath struck the firing pin, she heard an ear-splitting clang and felt a tremendous rush of air in her face. Every muscle in her body tightened, and she gripped the controls even harder. The Magnifico Falco lurched forwards and she felt her shoulder straps dig in. Amidst the rush of air all around her, Agnès heard Melzi calling out.

"Pull up, pull up," he was yelling. Agnès wrenched back hard on the levers. The Magnifico Falco jolted and shuddered. And then, like a fledgeling taking to the air for the first time, it mounted to the sky and flew free.

238

Easing back on the levers, Agnès soared steadily higher. She looked down and saw children dancing about in the streets below, waving up at her. She laughed out loud and yelled at the top of her voice.

"I'm flying, I'm flying!" she cried at Magellan who was soaring right alongside.

When the flying machine veered towards a rocky ridge, Agnès pushed with her right foot and steered it the other way. When it began to lose height, she pulled on the levers and it rose up again. Her heart raced. She wondered what her papa and mama would think if they could see her.

"What must the Birdman be feeling right now, seeing the Magnifico Falco flying towards him?" she thought.

As she looked ahead, Agnès could see the rooftops of Le Cloux, fast approaching. Its chimneys and spires were rushing up to greet her. She tried to work out which, of all the windows, was the Birdman's study. She hoped to spot him watching, with Maturina and King François by his side. But it was hard to see anything with the wind in her face. She gripped the control lever tightly and tried to find a good place to land. Her thoughts were to fly right over the rooftop, then swoop down to the lawn, where she could touch down safely.

When she felt the Magnifico Falco veer off course, she pushed with her foot. The flying machine flew the other way. The left wing lifted unexpectedly, and Agnès felt it swoop dangerously close to the treetops. Pushing with her other foot, she just managed to avoid clipping the branches. She skirted past the manor house and soared over the lawn. Sheep scattered in every direction, and pecking birds flew up in a wild frenzy.

The flying machine was falling fast. Agnès leaned back in her harness. She pulled hard on both levers and shut her eyes tight. The Magnifico Falco was more than halfway across the lawn. The enormous plane tree at the end of the garden was looming large. Its branches reached out like the arms of a giant, ready to catch her. At the very last moment, Agnès let go of the controls and covered her face with her arms. The flying machine shook and twisted. Agnès felt herself being pulled and plucked from the belly of the bird. She whirled about in a wild commotion. When she opened her eyes and looked up, she could see a great tangle of twisted wings and struts. Wrapped in rags of blue silk, the Magnifico Falco was swaying in the branches above her head.

When Agnès heard a voice, she craned her neck and saw Hugo hurrying across the lawn with a long ladder balanced on his shoulder. Resting it against the tree, the watchman climbed up and released Agnès from her tangle of ropes and straps. Carrying her over his shoulder, he lifted her down to the lawn below. Agnès was shaking from head to toe. She looked back up at the Magnifico Falco, then flung her arms around the watchman's neck and kissed him.

"It flies!" she yelled. "It really flies!" Excitedly, she set off over the lawn towards the manor house.

"Mademoiselle Agnès, wait," called out Hugo. But Agnès was in too much of a hurry. She ran across the lawn, her feet flying, and her heart pounding. When she reached the manor house, she hurried up the stairs. At the top, she made her way along the landing to the Birdman's study where he would be sitting by the window, having watched the whole thing from the comfort of his armchair. But, when she pushed the door open and went inside, the shutters were closed and the room was shrouded in darkness. Across the way, in the far corner of the room, was a thin sliver of light. It was coming from the crack beneath the door that led into the Master's bedchamber.

Stumbling and bumping into tables as she went, Agnès made her way over to the door. Turning the handle, she pushed it open and went inside. Solemn faces, lit by the glow of burning candles, looked around as she walked into the room.

The Birdman lay beneath his covers, propped up on a mound of pillows. A priest was reading from the Holy Book. The King, Maturina and the Royal Physician looked on. Agnès walked over and stood by the Master's bedside. His eyes were open. She saw his lips tremble and he started to mutter. The Birdman pointed a quivering finger.

"Do you see them?" he said feebly.

"What do you see, my friend?" King François asked.

"The birds—do you see them?" said the Master.

"You must rest," said the King. "It's time for you to sleep." The old man drew breath.

"Where are the birds taking me?" he said. Agnès remembered the Birdman's dream. She thought about his vision of white gulls that had carried him across the sea to the city in the mountains, where he had met the Golden King.

King François stepped forwards and gently laid a hand on the Master's forehead.

"You are safe here," he said. "You are with friends." The Birdman looked at Agnès. He gazed deep into her eyes, and his lips parted.

"Agnès, is that you?" he said. Agnès knelt by the bedside.

"Yes, it's me," she said. "I'm here." The Birdman reached out.

"Were my works good enough?" he asked. Agnès felt warm tears well up in her eyes. She squeezed his hand tightly and nodded.

"Yes, your works were good enough," she replied. "The Magnifico Falco flew just as you always dreamt it would." The Birdman smiled. As his eyes closed for the last time, Agnès felt his hand slip from hers. She sank back and sobbed.

When she felt a hand on her shoulder, Agnès looked around.

It was King François.

"You must have been true friends," said the King. Agnès shook her head slowly.

"I didn't even know his name," she said, wiping away the tears. King François helped Agnès to her feet.

"One day, all the world will know his name," he said. "They will know of Leonardo Da Vinci and will praise his great works forever more."

38

gnès sat by the riverside, listening to the lapping of the water and the cry of the gulls. Taking out her father's journal, she read again the last few pages. It was the day her papa and Signor Suarez finally reached the City of Gold.

November Tenth 1514

We bade farewell at sundown and commenced our long journey back down the mountainside. A thousand biting insects have plagued us like invisible demons. Progress has been far slower than expected. We camped by a river and lit a fire to ward off the forest creatures.

November Twelfth 1514

Heavy rains have slowed our progress. It is impossible to stay dry, and we are chilled and hungry. The forest has all but drained us of our strength. With such aching and shivering in my bones, I pray I can go on. My greatest wish is to see Agnès again.

November Fourteenth 1514

*Fernando has come upon a dry cave where
we shall shelter from the rains until I am well
enough to continue. The jungle is dreadful. It has
all but conquered my body but not my spirit.
How I long to be back in my own dear country,
to see little Agnès again. I think of her every
day and pray that the sisters at the convent are
treating her well. There is so much I long to tell
her. My greatest hope is that Agnès forgives me
for leaving her such a very long time.*

"There's nothing to forgive," said Agnès softly. "Nothing
to forgive at all." She could only imagine what had happened
next and hoped that her papa's suffering had been short.

A week had passed since the flight of the Magnifico Falco
and the Birdman's death. When Agnès thought about all that
had happened—how she had flown through the sky like a
bird—she felt truly alive. In her quest to help the Birdman,
her eyes had been turned skyward. She no longer felt like a
thief or a runaway. People who stopped her in the streets now

called her *The Girl Who Flew*.

When the clocktower bell chimed, Agnès got up and walked along to the quayside. She spotted Melzi waiting there. He was carrying a large holdall over his shoulder and was gazing upstream. When Agnès called out, Melzi turned around.

"Agnès, you're here," he said. "I'm glad you came to see me off. I want to thank you for what you have done." Agnès shook her head.

"We did it together," she said. "We were a team." Melzi looked back along the river as a riverboat sailed to shore.

"I'm going home to my family," he said. "Now that the Master has gone, I have no reason to stay."

"They'll be so happy to see you," said Agnès.

"I've decided to open up a painting school," said Melzi.

"I expect it will the finest in all Milan," said Agnès. Opening his holdall, Melzi took out a small parcel.

"This for you," he said, "so that you don't forget."

Agnès unwrapped the parcel. Inside was a painting of the Magnifico Falco. It was a miniature masterpiece in every detail. Suspended below the flying machine was a girl in a yellow taffeta dress. Agnès smiled.

"It's beautiful," she said. "Thank you." She reached up on tip-toes and kissed Melzi on the cheek. She waved as he climbed aboard the riverboat. Melzi looked around one last time.

"Perhaps I'll be back one day," he called out.

A flock of white geese flew over the bridge of seven arches as Agnès turned and walked away. Following the path along to the Manor of Touraine, she recognised the place the moment she saw it. Just as Pepin had said, there were stone lions by the gates and an eagle on the rooftop.

Agnès waved to the gatekeeper and told him she was there to see Monsieur Balthasar—she had something very important to give him. The gatekeeper went off and came back a few minutes later with the big nobleman. He opened the gates and Monsieur Balthasar stepped out. Agnès held out her hand and unfurled her fingers.

"This belongs to you," she said. The big nobleman stared down. His red ruby pin lay glinting in the palm of her hand. Agnès looked the big nobleman in the eyes.

"I really am sorry," she said. "I've been meaning to give you this for a while."

The nobleman frowned.

"You're the girl who flew aren't you?" he said.

Agnès nodded.

"I was there," said Monsieur Balthasar. "I saw the whole thing."

"If you report me to Marshal Lupus, I'll completely understand," said Agnès. Monsieur Balthasar shook his head.

"Leonardo was a good friend of mine," he said. "He saw something noble in you—so let's not speak any more of it."

"Thank you," said Agnès, handing back the ruby. Monsieur

Balthasar pinned it to his cloak.

"It was a gift from him to me," he said. "He had it made especially."

As she turned and walked away, Agnès felt a great burden lift from her mind. The red ruby pin no longer weighed heavy in her heart and she felt as light as a feather.

Back at the market square, later on, Agnès spotted Pepin sitting by the water fountain. When she tapped him on the shoulder, he turned around.

"Agnès, you're here," said Pepin. "What took you so long?"

"I had a few things to take care of," said Agnès. Reaching into her pocket, she took out a handful of coins.

"Pepin, how would you like to do something wonderful?" she said.

"What like?" said Pepin. Agnès grabbed him by the arm.

"Come with me," she said. Across the way, the old birdwoman had set out her cages at the foot of the tower and was trying to get the attention of passers-by. Agnès led Pepin over. They prodded each cage in turn and listened to the birds chirping.

"Do you like birds?" said the shabby birdwoman.

Agnès smiled.

"How much do you want for them?"

"Two sous apiece."

"We'll take them all," said Agnès, holding out a handful of silver coins. She turned to Pepin.

"Lend me a hand," she said. Together they went around unclasping all the cage doors. The little birds chirped and flapped. One by one, they hopped onto the bars and stretched out their wings. Very soon, the sky was full of songbirds: buntings, babblers, nightingales and linnets—all of them flying free. Agnès smiled to see them go, and Pepin waved wildly as the birds flew off into the bright blue sky.

Leonardo Da Vinci

ive hundred years have passed since the death of the great artist and inventor, Leonardo Da Vinci. There can't be many people who don't know about his amazing works. His painting of Lisa, the wife of Francesco del Giocondo, is the most valuable in the world. It now hangs in the Louvre art gallery in Paris and is worth over six hundred million dollars.

In his lifetime, Leonardo not only painted beautiful artwork but also invented ingenious machines. It all started back in Florence, Italy. At the age of twelve, his father took him to that great city from the little town of Vinci, where he had lived with his grandparents. Leonardo went to school and worked hard. At the age of fourteen, he became an apprentice to Andrea del Verrocchio, after his father showed the artist and engineer some of his son's drawings. Verrocchio was astonished by Leonardo's talent. For the next six years, the young apprentice helped him finish some of his paintings. He also created sculptures and built scenery for stage plays. To bring the scenery to life, he used pulleys and ropes, gears and clever mechanisms to make angels fly and fantastical creatures move about. Leonardo liked to dress in colourful clothing and designed costumes for actors to wear. He also developed a new way of painting, called sfumato. He used this method to paint beautiful faces and soft flowing fabrics.

For many years, Leonardo moved back and forth between Florence and Milan. At the age of forty-six, he built his first flying machine. His attempt to fly was a failure. Seven years later, he tried again, getting his apprentice to leap from a hill at Monte Cicero. Although his experiments were unsuccessful, similar gliders were flown by pioneers in aviation such as Otto Lilienthal, the *Flying Man*, almost four hundred years later.

When the King of France, François I, came to Italy to fight the Swiss, he saw some of Leonardo's work. On many occasions, the King pleaded with him to come to France and serve as his chief artist and inventor.

In 1516, at the age of sixty-four, Leonardo finally agreed. Travelling by donkey across the Alps, and carrying three of his favourite paintings, he came to live in France at the Manor of Le Cloux in the town of Amboise. Every day, the King would visit, often just to hear the sound of his voice. Leonardo put on great banquets for the King and Queen. One time, he painted the sun, moon and planets on great sheets of blue fabric that were hung in the courtyard. The great montage was illuminated by four hundred candelabras that turned night into day. On another occasion, he built a mechanical lion that could walk, open wide its jaws and swish its tail. When the belly of the beast opened up, the King was astonished to see bunches of lilies inside. During his time at Le Cloux, Leonardo grew weak and frail. He looked older than he really was. He died on May

2nd 1519, lying in his bed. In his final few moments, knowing that he was about to die, he sat up and lamented that he feared his works were not good enough.

Francesco De Melzi

Of all the apprentices Leonardo took on, Melzi was the one who stayed with him to the very end. He was born in Italy and accompanied him on his journey across the Alps in 1516. Melzi was said to be charming and graceful and had good manners. He was tall and had long auburn hair. Leonardo first met the boy, aged fourteen, when he stayed with Melzi's family in Milan. This was also the time Leonardo first experimented with flight and built a flying machine. Melzi was taught to paint and became a very good artist. He was responsible for some of the paintings that were later thought to be Leonardo's.

After his Master's death, Melzi went back to Italy where he worked hard to collect and organise his works. He wrote a book containing many of Leonardo's thoughts and ideas. He married and had eight children, one of whom inherited Leonardo's many drawings.

Maturina

Maturina was Leonardo's cook and housekeeper while he lived at the Manor of Le Cloux in France. She is mentioned is in his last will and testament, which he wrote a year before he died.

> *The said Testator gives to Maturina, his waiting-woman, a cloak of good black cloth lined with fur, and two ducats paid once only; and this likewise is in remuneration for good service rendered to him in past times by the said Maturina.*

It is very likely that Maturina was a local French woman from Amboise, rather than someone who came with him from Italy. She would have had others to help her in the kitchen and around the house. Leonardo was a vegetarian so the meals she prepared for him would have been very different from the banquets and feasts she prepared for the King and Queen.

Anne Boleyn

Anne was the second wife of King Henry VIII of England and the mother of Queen Elizabeth I. When she was young, she served for seven years as Maid of Honour to Queen Claude of France. She was slim, had long dark hair, brown eyes and an olive complexion. She was clever and funny but sometimes had a bad temper. Her interests were many, including archery, falconry and playing bowls. At the court of King Francis I, she gained an education in many of the arts and French culture.

Three years after Leonardo's death in 1519, Anne sailed home to England. Following a seven-year courtship with the King of England, Henry VIII, she was married and crowned Queen in 1533. Later that year, in September, her only daughter Elizabeth was born. King Henry was bitterly disappointed. He wanted a son and heir to the throne. When Anne's only surviving child was a daughter, the irate King accused her of using spells and deception to marry him.

At the age of thirty-five, Anne was executed at the Tower of London, and the King was free to marry again. Dressed in a green gown, she stepped onto a platform and made a speech. She was then beheaded by a French swordsman according to the wishes of the King.

King Francis I

rancis never expected to be crowned King of France. When his cousin, Louis XII, died without a son and heir to the throne, the title fell to him. Knowing that Francis would succeed him, a marriage was arranged with King Louis' daughter, Claude, who was just fifteen years old at the time.

Francis was tall, handsome and athletic. He was also a hero in battle. Some called him *The Knight King*. Others gave him the name, *Francis of the Large Nose*.

After the Battle of Marignano, during the Italian wars, he led a victorious cavalry charge. Francis banqueted and feasted with the Pope following the victory. It was then that he invited the great artist, Leonardo Da Vinci, to return with him to France. He gave Leonardo the title of *First Painter, Architect, and Engineer to the King* and granted him seven hundred gold crowns a year, as well as the use of the Manor of Le Cloux, where he had grown up as a boy.

After Leonardo's death, Francis travelled widely around his kingdom on horseback. For many French people, it was the first time they had ever met a King. He went to battle against his lifelong rival, King Charles V of Spain. After a great defeat in 1525, he was captured and held for a year in Madrid. In his prison cell, he wrote poems, songs and letters home. At this time, great tragedy befell the King when his beloved Queen

Claude died, aged just twenty-four. Together they had seven children.

Francis was keen to send ships to the Americas where colonies were being settled by his rivals. He founded the port of Franciscopolis—now called Le Havre—and had French explorers sail across the Atlantic Ocean to Newfoundland, claiming it for the French Crown. During his reign, new religious beliefs were spreading across Europe. At first, Francis was friendly towards the Protestant reformers. Later in his life, however, he turned against them. He grew weak and ill and died at the age of fifty-two in the year 1547.

About the Author

Tuscany, Italy – AD 1505
Upon a rocky ledge, high above Swan Mountain quarry, there perched a peculiar bird of wood and sailcloth. Ropes creaked. Broad wings swayed. Struts bent and flexed with every gust and flurry as the curious contraption teetered over the abyss.
Harnessed beneath the belly of the bird, a skinny youth held on tightly, awaiting his master's command. The boy looked to the sky where a dark raven circled with steely eyes and piercing caws that echoed all through the quarry below.

Stephen Münzer is an author and illustrator of craft books and magazines that inspire children to build their own creations. In this, his first novel, he tells the story of a young girl who helps an ageing artist and inventor to realise his life-long dream of building a flying machine. Stephen lives in York, England, with his wife Christine. He has four children and three sparky granddaughters.

www.munzer.co.uk

Stephen Allinson is an author and illustrator of truth books and magazines that inspire children to build their own creations. In this, his first novel, he tells the story of a young girl who helps an ageing artist and inventor to realise his life-long dream of building a flying machine. Stephen lives in York, England, with his wife Christine. He has four children and three sturdy granddaughters.

Follow Agnès's journey

facebook.com/agnesandthebirdman